Test Generator Assessment
Item Listing

D1472245

HOLT, RINEHART AND WINSTON

A Harcourt Classroom Education Company

Holt Science Spectrum: A Physical Approach
Test Generator Assessment Item Listing

Cover: basketball image: David Madison/Tony Stone; celestial background image: Corbis Images.

Printed in the United States of America

ISBN 0-03-055587-6

2 3 4 5 179 03 02 01 00

Contents

Chapters   Holt Science Spectrum: A Physical Approach

About the Test Generator and Test Item Listing

The *Holt Science Spectrum: A Physical Approach* Test Generator contains a range of assessment and review options for *Holt Science and Technology*. For each chapter in the textbook, the Test Generator contains chapter test questions, including multiple choice, short answer, and essay questions. The Test Generator allows you to generate custom-made tests by selecting only those items you want from the many items available. For easy reference, this *Test Generator: Assessment Item Listing* contains a complete printout of all items stored on the Test Generator portion of the *Holt Science Spectrum: A Physical Approach One-Stop Planner CD-ROM*. The Test Generator program and chapter files are stored on the *One-Stop Planner CD-ROM*. The Test Generator User's Guide is also part of the *One-Stop Planner CD-ROM*. The files are described below.

Chapter Files

Items are stored in chapter files, each of which corresponds to a chapter in your textbook.

Information Fields

When you view chapter files in the Test Generator, you will notice several information fields above each item. A description of these fields follows the example below.

ITEM TYPE: Multiple Choice   OBJECTIVE: 1–1
LEVEL: none   TAG: None

In a scientific experiment, a hypothesis that cannot be tested is always considered:

A. incorrect.   C. not useful.
B. illogical.   D. a theory.

Item type: The Test Generator is designed to allow selection of items by type. Item types include, but are not limited to, the following:

- Multiple Choice
- True or False
- Short Answer
- Essay Questions

Level: Items provided in the Test Generator are classified by difficulty level. Consult the *HRW Test Generator User's Guide,* located on the *One-Stop Planner CD-ROM,* for instructions on using this feature of the program.

Objective: The field refers to the corresponding textbook section and objection number.

Tag: A tag indicates that when you generate a test, a graphic or special set of instructions will print with the tagged test item. Several test items will carry the same tag if the items are related. The tags in each chapter file on the *One-Stop Planner CD-ROM* appear at the end of the chapter listing.

Answer: In the Test Generator, an answer immediately follows a test item. A small black box appears in the lower right corner of the answer box for easy identification.

Editing and Writing Test Questions

The Test Generator program allows you to edit the items in the chapter files as well as write your own questions; however, the CD-ROM is a read-only disc. In order to edit or add test items to a chapter file, you must first copy the file to your computer's hard drive or to a diskette. The *HRW Test Generator User's Guide* on the *One-Stop Planner CD-ROM* describes these features of the program in detail.

Technical Support

The *HRW Test Generator User's Guide* will answer most questions you have about the Test Generator program. If you need additional assistance, call the Holt, Rinehart and Winston Technical Support Center at 1-800-323-9239. You can also access a knowledge base of solutions to common problems and answers to common questions by calling the Technical Support Center's Fax-on-Demand Service at 1-800-352-1680.

In addition, you can contact the Technical Support Center through the World Wide Web at http://www.hrwtechsupport.com or by E-mail at tsc@hrwtechsupport.com.

Installation for the Test Generator

The *Holt Science Spectrum: A Physical Approach* Test Generator is a special version of the TestBuilder program. Although the User's Guide contains directions for installing the program, it is suggested that you follow the installation directions below.

Macintosh Installation

The TestBuilder installer copies the TestBuilder program to your hard drive and installs the fonts that the program uses. When installing TestBuilder, you can choose between Easy Installation or Custom Installation. Most users will want to do the Easy Installation. Choose Custom Installation only if you want to select the type of fonts to be installed on your computer.

1. Insert the *Holt Science Spectrum: A Physical Approach One-Stop Planner CD-ROM* into your CD-ROM drive. When the disc's icon appears on the screen, double-click the icon to open the CD-ROM. A window will open, showing the contents of the CD-ROM.

2. Locate the Holt TestBuilder Installer icon, and double-click it. This will launch the installer program.

3. For Easy Installation, when the Installer menu appears, click on the Install button and follow the on-screen directions. For Custom Installation, when the Installer menu appears, click and hold the Easy Install button at the top of the menu. Choose Custom Install from the drop-down menu. Select a font, click the Install button, and follow the on-screen directions.

TestBuilder fonts: The Installer installs the fonts used by the TestBuilder program. The Easy Installation automatically installs Type 1 fonts, which work on most Macintosh computers. If your computer does not have the Adobe Type Manager extension, then you should use the Custom Installation to install the TrueType fonts.

Windows 95, 98, and NT Installation

1. Insert the *Holt Science Spectrum: A Physical Approach One-Stop Planner CD-ROM* into your CD-ROM drive.

2. Click the Start button, and then click Run.

3. In the Open box, type d:\tbsetup (substitute the letter for your CD-ROM drive if it is not named "d").

4. Click OK, and follow the directions on the screen.

Getting Started

Once you have installed the TestBuilder program, follow the directions in the User's Guide to start the program, create tests, and use the other features available. The User's Guide includes a tutorial to help you get acquainted with the program.

Locating the Chapter Files on the CD-ROM

When you are ready to use the Test Generator, insert the CD-ROM and locate the chapter files. The chapter files are stored in Macintosh and Windows folders.

Macintosh users: Open the MacTests folder on the CD-ROM. Each MacTests file contains questions, problems and other items for each textbook chapter. The filenames identify the chapter.

Windows users: Open the WinTests folder on the CD-ROM. Each WinTests file contains questions, problems and other items for each textbook chapter. The filenames identify the chapter.

Copying Files to Your Hard Drive

If you wish to edit the file questions or add questions of your own, you must first copy the files from the CD-ROM onto your computer's hard drive. Changes cannot be made to files on the *One-Stop Planner CD-ROM*.

Chapter 1

1) Item Type: Multiple Choice Objective: 1-1.1
  Level: I   Tag: None

The two main branches of science are

   a) physics and chemistry.   b) natural and social science.

   c) natural and physical science. d) biological and earth science.

b

2) Item Type: Multiple Choice Objective: 1-1.1
  Level: I   Tag: None

Which of the following is *not* a branch of biology?

   a) geology   b) ecology

   c) zoology   d) medicine

a

3) Item Type: Multiple Choice Objective: 1-1.1
  Level: I   Tag: None

The main branches of natural science are

   a) physics and chemistry.   b) biology, zoology, and
             ecology.

   c) medicine and agriculture. d) life, physical, and earth
             science.

d

4) Item Type: Multiple Choice Objective: 1-1.2
  Level: I   Tag: None

Technology can best be defined as

   a) science that uses computers. b) new inventions.

   c) applied science.   d) the use of lenses and
             microscopes.

c

5) Item Type: Multiple Choice Objective: 1-1.2
Level: I Tag: None

Pure science is best defined as the

a) continuing search for new knowledge.
b) use of science to solve human problems.
c) study of the makeup of living things.
d) application of scientific knowledge.

a

6) Item Type: Multiple Choice Objective: 1-1.2
Level: I Tag: None

What do scientists who do pure science do?

a) They look for ways to use scientific knowledge to solve problems.
b) They develop new uses for scientific knowledge.
c) They do experiments to find out about the world.
d) They build faster and more powerful computers.

c

7) Item Type: Multiple Choice Objective: 1-1.3
Level: I Tag: None

A scientific theory is an explanation that

a) has been published in a journal or book.
b) predicts what will happen.
c) has been tested by many observations.
d) a scientist has tested with an experiment.

c

8) Item Type: Multiple Choice Objective: 1-1.3
Level: I Tag: None

What is a scientific law?

a) It is the same as a hypothesis.
b) It is a description of a natural event.
c) It is an explanation of a scientific observation.
d) It is the conclusion of a scientific experiment.

b

9) Item Type: Multiple Choice   Objective: 1-1.3
    Level: I   Tag: None

    For a scientific theory to be valid, it must allow you to

                a) perform experiments.   b) obtain new results each
                                                 time.

                c) find a new, more complex   d) make predictions.
                explanation.

    d

10) Item Type: Multiple Choice   Objective: 1-1.4
    Level: I   Tag: None

    A scientific model is a

                a) representation of a real   b) small building used to conduct
                event or object.   experiments.

                c) mathematical statement of   d) new theory that takes the
                a theory.   place of an incorrect one.

    a

11) Item Type: Multiple Choice   Objective: 1-1.3
    Level: I   Tag: None

    Scientific theories can be changed or replaced when

                a) new technology is invented.   b) new discoveries are made.

                c) scientists decide to work on d) scientists make models of
                different problems.   events or objects.

    b

12) Item Type: Multiple Choice   Objective: 1-1.4
    Level: I   Tag: None

    Scientists use computer models to study complicated events and to

                a) perform experiments.   b) state theories.

                c) change theories and laws.   d) make predictions.

    d

Chapter 1

13) Item Type: Multiple Choice   Objective: 1-2.1
    Level: I   Tag: None

A series of logical steps that is followed in order to solve a problem is called the

        a) experimental process.   b) scientific theory.

        c) scientific method.   d) model method.

c

14) Item Type: Multiple Choice   Objective: 1-1.2
    Level: I   Tag: None

The first step in the scientific method is usually

        a) making an observation.   b) forming a hypothesis.

        c) collecting data.   d) testing a hypothesis.

a

15) Item Type: Multiple Choice   Objective: 1-2.1
    Level: I   Tag: None

Scientists test a hypothesis by

        a) formulating questions.   b) designing models.

        c) doing experiments.   d) drawing conclusions.

c

16) Item Type: Multiple Choice   Objective: 1-2.1
    Level: I   Tag: None

What does it mean to say that "no experiment is a failure"?

        a) All experiments are observations of real events.   b) All experiments yield the desired results.

        c) All experiments give scientists work to do.   d) All experiments involve manipulating variables.

a

17) Item Type: Multiple Choice   Objective: 1-2.1
    Level: I   Tag: None

Which instrument has been used to detect the oldest, most distant objects in the solar system?

a) light telescope   b) spectrophotometer

c) particle accelerator   d) radio telescope

d

18) Item Type: Multiple Choice   Objective: 1-2.1
    Level: II   Tag: None

Which question *cannot* be answered by an experiment?

a) Does penicillin kill   b) Is rabies caused by a
Salmonella bacteria?   virus?

c) Did a comet impact kill the d) Can radiation cause
dinosaurs?   cancer?

c

19) Item Type: Multiple Choice   Objective: 1-2.2
    Level: I   Tag: None

The SI unit for measuring temperature is the

a) degree.   b) kelvin.

c) mole.   d) ampere.

b

20) Item Type: Multiple Choice   Objective: 1-2.2
    Level: I   Tag: None

Which SI prefix means one million?

a) kilo-   b) mega-

c) giga-   d) milli-

b

21) Item Type: Multiple Choice   Objective: 1-2.2
    Level: I   Tag: None

Which SI prefix means one one-hundredth (1/100)?

        a) nano-   b) micro-

        c) milli-   d) centi-

d

22) Item Type: Multiple Choice   Objective: 1-2.2
    Level: II   Tag: None

Maria is 123 centimeters tall. Her height in meters is

        a) 0123 m.   b) .123 m.

        c) 1.23 m.   d) 12.3 m.

c

23) Item Type: Multiple Choice   Objective: 1-2.2
    Level: II   Tag: None

A loaf of bread weighs 1362 g. The weight in kilograms is

        a) 1.362 kg.   b) 1362 kg.

        c) 01362 kg.   d) 001362 kg.

a

24) Item Type: Multiple Choice   Objective: 1-2.2
    Level: I   Tag: None

The force with which gravity pulls on a quantity of matter is referred to as

        a) mass.   b) length.

        c) volume.   d) weight.

d

25) Item Type: Multiple Choice   Objective: 1-3.1
    Level: II   Tag: ES-1

At which time of day was the temperature approximately 4 degrees C?

        a) 9:00 A.M.   b) 10:00 A.M.

        c) 11:00 A.M.   d) 12:00 P.M.

b

26) Item Type: Multiple Choice   Objective: 1-3.1
Level: II   Tag: ES-1

At which two times of day was the temperature the same?

         a) 7:00 A.M. and 7:00 P.M.   b) 7:00 A.M. and 10:00

         c) 10:00 A.M. and 7:00 P.M.   d) 10:00 a.m. and 10:00 p.m.

27) Item Type: Multiple Choice   Objective: 1-3.1
Level: II   Tag: ES-2

The sample contained the same number of pennies for which two years?

         a) 1988 and 1992   b) 1988 and 1991

         c) 1994 and 1997   d) 1994 and 1998

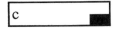

28) Item Type: Multiple Choice   Objective: 1-3.1
Level: II   Tag: ES-2

For which year was the smallest number of pennies found?

         a) 1988   b) 1989

         c) 1990   d) 1991

29) Item Type: Multiple Choice   Objective: 1-3.3
Level: II   Tag: None

The decimal equivalent of 10^{-2} is

         a) 100.   b) 10.

         c) 0.1.   d) 0.01.

30) Item Type: Multiple Choice   Objective: 1-3.3
Level: II   Tag: None

What is 78,900,000,000 expressed in scientific notation?

         a) 789×10^9 b) 78.9×10^8

         c) 78.9×10^9 d) 78.9×10^{10}

31) Item Type: Multiple Choice   Objective: 1-3.3
     Level: II   Tag: None

The speed of light is approximately 3×10^8 m/s. How would this be written in conventional notation?

   a) 300,000 m/s   b) 3,000,000 m/s

   c) 30,000,000 m/s   d) 300,000,000 m/s

d

32) Item Type: Multiple Choice   Objective: 1-3.2
     Level: II   Tag: None

You are asked to find the area of a room that is 4.56 m long and 5.668 m wide. How many significant figures should you show in your answer?

   a) 3   b) 5

   c) 6   d) 7

a

33) Item Type: Multiple Choice   Objective: 1-3.2
     Level: II   Tag: None

You are asked to find the volume of a cube that is 2.5 cm high, 2.65 cm wide, and 3.456 cm long. How many significant figures should you show in your answer?

   a) 1   b) 2

   c) 3   d) 4

b

34) Item Type: Multiple Choice   Objective: 1-3.2
     Level: II   Tag: None

What is the volume of a room that is 4×10^2 cm long and 2×10^3 cm wide?

   a) 6×10^3 cm^2 b) 8×10^3 cm^2

   c) 8×10^5 cm^2 d) 8×10^7 cm^2

c

35) Item Type: Multiple Choice   Objective: 1-3.4
Level: I   Tag: None

A precise measurement is one that

    a) contains the correct number of significant figures.   b) contains at least three significant figures.

    c) is close to the true value.   d) is as exact as possible.

d

36) Item Type: Multiple Choice   Objective: 1-3.4
Level: I   Tag: None

A measurement that is accurate is one that

    a) is as exact as possible.   b) is close to the true value.

    c) contains at least four significant figures.   d) contains five decimal places.

b

37) Item Type: Short Answer   Objective: 1-1.1
Level: I   Tag: None

Chemistry and physics are the two branches of _____ science.

physical

38) Item Type: Short Answer   Objective: 1-1.1
Level: I   Tag: None

Wilhelm Roentgen discovered _____ while he was investigating cathode rays.

X-rays

39) Item Type: Short Answer   Objective: 1-1.1
Level: I   Tag: None

Life science, physical science, and earth science make up _____ science.

natural

40) Item Type: Short Answer   Objective: 1-1.2
Level: I   Tag: None

Pure science is the continuing search for scientific _____.

knowledge

41) Item Type: Short Answer   Objective: 1-1.2
    Level: 1   Tag: None

The application of science to meet human needs is referred to as _____.

technology

42) Item Type: Short Answer   Objective: 1-1.2
    Level: 1   Tag: None

Scientists depend on _____ to find practical uses for their discoveries.

engineers

43) Item Type: Short Answer   Objective: 1-1.3
    Level: 1   Tag: None

A theory is a scientific _____ for a natural event.

explanation

44) Item Type: Short Answer   Objective: 1-1.3
    Level: 1   Tag: None

A scientific _____ describes a natural event but does not explain why the event

law

45) Item Type: Short Answer   Objective: 1-1.3
    Level: 1   Tag: None

A _____ description of a scientific law would use a mathematical equation.

quantitative

46) Item Type: Short Answer   Objective: 1-1.3
    Level: 1   Tag: None

Theories are sometimes replaced as a result of new _____.

discoveries

47) Item Type: Short Answer   Objective: 1-1.4
    Level: 1   Tag: None

A mathematical representation of an object or event is a _____.

model

48) Item Type: Short Answer   Objective: 1-1.4
    Level: 1   Tag: None

Scientists use models to represent real situations and to make _____.

predictions

49) Item Type: Short Answer   Objective: 1-2.1
Level: 1   Tag: None

The scientific method gives scientists a way to _____ their thinking about a problem or question.

organize

50) Item Type: Short Answer   Objective: 1-2.1
Level: 1   Tag: None

A possible answer to a scientific problem is called a _____.

hypothesis

51) Item Type: Short Answer   Objective: 1-2.1
Level: 1   Tag: None

To view objects that are very small, a scientist would use a _____ _____.

light microscope

52) Item Type: Short Answer   Objective: 1-2.1
Level: 1   Tag: None

Any factor in an experiment that can change is referred to as a _____.

variable

53) Item Type: Short Answer   Objective: 1-2.1
Level: 1   Tag: None

Physicists use _____ _____ to make pieces of atoms move extremely fast and collide with one another.

particle accelerators

54) Item Type: Short Answer   Objective: 1-2.1
Level: 1   Tag: None

Scientists test a hypothesis by making _____.

observations

55) Item Type: Short Answer   Objective: 1-2.1
Level: 1   Tag: None

Length, mass, time, and temperature, are four of the seven SI _____ _____.

base units

Chapter 1

56) Item Type: Short Answer   Objective: 1-2.2
Level: I   Tag: None

Combinations of the SI base units, which are used to measure quantities such as volume, speed, and pressure, are called _____ _____.

derived units ◼

57) Item Type: Short Answer   Objective: 1-2.2
Level: I   Tag: None

In the SI system, the prefix _____ means one billion.

giga- ◼

58) Item Type: Short Answer   Objective: 1-2.1
Level: I   Tag: None

In the SI system, the prefix _____ means one millionth.

micro- ◼

59) Item Type: Short Answer   Objective: 1-2.2
Level: II   Tag: None

375 cm equals _____ m.

3.75 ◼

60) Item Type: Short Answer   Objective: 1-2.2
Level: II   Tag: None

5675 g equals _____ kg.

5.675 ◼

61) Item Type: Short Answer   Objective: 1-3.1
Level: II   Tag: ES-3

The most abundant gas in the atmosphere is _____.

nitrogen ◼

62) Item Type: Short Answer   Objective: 1-3.1
Level: II   Tag: ES-3

The proportion of oxygen in the atmosphere is closest to _____ percent.

20 ◼

63) Item Type: Short Answer   Objective: 1-3.1
Level: I   Tag: None

Line graphs are most effective at displaying data that _____ _____.

change continuously

64) Item Type: Short Answer   Objective: 1-3.1
Level: I   Tag: None

The best kind of graph to make to show the density of a number of different substances, would be a _____ _____.

bar graph

65) Item Type: Short Answer   Objective: 1-3.2
Level: II   Tag: None

The number .0034 would be written as 3.4 times _____ in scientific notation.

10^{-3}

66) Item Type: Short Answer   Objective: 1-3.2
Level: II   Tag: None

In scientific notation, the number 46,500,000 would be written _____.

46.5×10^6

67) Item Type: Short Answer   Objective: 1-3.2
Level: II   Tag: None

The number .0009234 would be written in scientific notation as _____ x _____.

9.234×10^{-4}

68) Item Type: Short Answer   Objective: 1-3.2
Level: II   Tag: None

The number 56,780,000,000 would be written in scientific notation as _____ x _____.

56.78×10^9

69) Item Type: Short Answer   Objective: 1-3.1
Level: II   Tag: None

The number 4.065 has _____ significant figures.

four

70) Item Type: Short Answer   Objective: 1-3.3
      Level: II   Tag: None

The number 50.775 has _____ significant figures.

five

71) Item Type: Short Answer   Objective: 1-3.4
      Level: I   Tag: None

The extent to which a measurement approaches the true value is referred to as

_____.

accuracy

72) Item Type: Short Answer   Objective: 1-3.4
      Level: I   Tag: None

Although a measurement of 6.13457902 cm is very _____, it may not be accurate.

precise

73) Item Type: Essay   Objective: 1-1.1, 1-2.1
      Level: II   Tag: None

List and explain the steps in the scientific method by using one of the famous discoveries described in the chapter as an example.

Wilhelm Roentgen was investigating the properties of cathode rays. He wondered if the rays could pass through a glass tube (question). He designed an apparatus to test this (collect data). He found that the rays were visible much longer than he expected. This caused him to formulate a new question and a new series of observations to determine what the new rays were.

74) Item Type: Essay   Objective: 1-1.1
      Level: III   Tag: None

"As science has progressed, the branches of science have merged together." Explain this statement.

As more discoveries are made about the nature of matter and energy, different sciences become interconnected. For example, biochemistry studies the chemistry of living things. Geophysics studies the forces that affect the earth.

75) Item Type: Essay   Objective: 1-1.3
Level: III   Tag: None

Explain why a scientific theory might be changed or replaced. Give an example of a law that was changed.

Scientific laws need to be changed as new discoveries are made. For example, caloric theory seemed to explain heat until the effects of friction were discovered. Then a new theory, kinetic theory, was developed to include the new information.

76) Item Type: Essay   Objective: 1-1.2
Level: III   Tag: None

Describe the relationship between science and technology, and give an example of how they are related.

Science involves making discoveries about the world, and technology involves finding practical uses for those discoveries. Sometimes science precedes technology, and sometimes it's the other way around. For example, microorganisms were not discovered until usable lenses were invented.

77) Item Type: Essay   Objective: 1-1.2
Level: III   Tag: None

What does it mean to say that "no experiment is a failure"? Do you agree or disagree? Why?

No experiment is a failure because, even if an experiment does not give the expected results, its results will lead to new questions and new observations. [Student should give a reason for the opinion expressed.]

78) Item Type: Essay   Objective: 1-3.1
Level: III   Tag: None

Why are organizing and presenting data important scientific skills?

Scientists need to read and find out about other scientists' work so they know what questions to ask and what observations to test. To do this, data must be presented and organized clearly and logically.

79) Item Type: Essay   Objective: 1-3.1
Level: III   Tag: None

Explain why scientists use scientific notation.

Scientists often need to express data using numbers that are very small or very large. Scientific notation, which eliminates a lot of zeroes and expresses numbers in terms of powers of 10, helps them do this efficiently.

80) Item Type: Essay   Objective: 1-3.4
    Level: III   Tag: None

"That measurement is very precise, but it is still not accurate." Explain how this statement might be true.

Suppose you were measuring a room. You might measure the length at 3.452389 m. This is a very precise measurement. However, if you wrote down the numbers incorrectly and the actual length was 4.452389, your measurement would not be accurate.

1)   Tag Name: ES-1

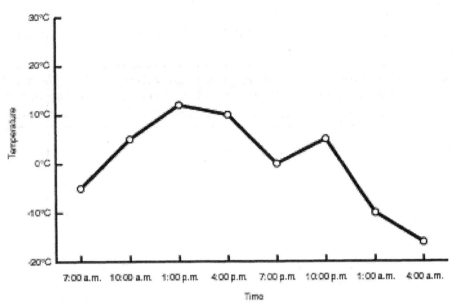

Temperature Measured Over Time

2)   Tag Name: ES-2

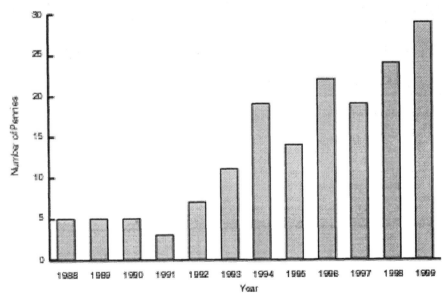

Temperature Measured Over Time

3)   Tag Name: ES-3

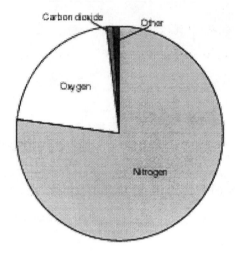

Chapter 2

1) Item Type: Multiple Choice   Objective: 2-1.1
   Level: I   Tag: None

   Matter is defined as anything that

          a) can be seen and touched.   b) has mass and takes up space.

          c) can be weighed.   d) contains kinetic or potential energy.

   b

2) Item Type: Multiple Choice   Objective: 2-1.2
   Level: I   Tag: None

   A substance that cannot be broken down into simpler substances is

          a) a compound.   b) a mixture.

          c) an element.   d) an atom.

   c

3) Item Type: Multiple Choice   Objective: 2-1.3
   Level: I   Tag: None

   The chemical formula for water, H_2O, means that each water molecule contains

          a) two hydrogen atoms and two oxygen atoms.   b) two hydrogen atoms and one oxygen atom.

          c) two hydrogen atoms and zero oxygen atoms.   d) one hydrogen atom and two oxygen atoms.

   b

4) Item Type: Multiple Choice   Objective: 2-1.4
   Level: I   Tag: None

   You put 1 gram of salt into 1 liter of water and stir. The resulting liquid is an example of

          a) a pure substance.   b) a heterogeneous mixture.

          c) a homogeneous mixture.   d) an immiscible mixture.

   c

5) Item Type: Multiple Choice   Objective: 2-1.1
   Level: I   Tag: None

   The science of what matter is made of and how it changes is called

          a) chemistry.   b) physics.

          c) kinetics.   d) engineering.

   a

6) Item Type: Multiple Choice   Objective: 2-1.1
    Level: I   Tag: None

    The chemical element that is most abundant in the human body is

                a) nitrogen.   b) iron.

                c) carbon.   d) oxygen.

    | d |

7) Item Type: Multiple Choice   Objective: 2-1.2
    Level: I   Tag: None

    The smallest unit of a substance that behaves like the substance is

                a) an element.   b) an atom.

                c) a molecule.   d) a compound.

    | c |

8) Item Type: Multiple Choice   Objective: 2-1.2
    Level: I   Tag: None

    The element that is most abundant in the Earth is

                a) iron.   b) oxygen.

                c) silicon.   d) magnesium.

    | a |

9) Item Type: Multiple Choice   Objective: 2-1.3
    Level: II   Tag: None

    The chemical symbol for sulfuric acid is H_2SO_4. How many atoms are contained in each molecule of sulfuric acid?

                a) 3   b) 5

                c) 6   d) 7

    | d |

10) Item Type: Multiple Choice   Objective: 2-1.3
    Level: I   Tag: None

    The chemical formula for table sugar is $C_{12}H_{22}O_{11}$. How many oxygen atoms are in each sugar molecule?

                a) 2   b) 11

                c) 12   d) 22

    | b |

11) Item Type: Multiple Choice   Objective: 2-1.4
    Level: I   Tag: None

A material that can be represented by a chemical formula is

a) an element.   b) a mixture.

c) a homogeneous solution.   d) a pure substance.

d

12) Item Type: Multiple Choice   Objective: 2-1.4
    Level: I   Tag: None

Which of the following is an example of a gas-liquid mixture?

a) the air we breathe   b) a carbonated drink

c) soapsuds   d) ice cubes

b

13) Item Type: Multiple Choice   Objective: 2-2.1
    Level: I   Tag: None

The resistance of a fluid to flow is referred to as

a) pressure.   b) energy.

c) viscosity.   d) shape.

c

14) Item Type: Multiple Choice   Objective: 2-2.1
    Level: I   Tag: None

Which state of matter will hold its shape without a container?

a) solid   b) liquid

c) gas   d) plasma

a

15) Item Type: Multiple Choice   Objective: 2-2.1
    Level: I   Tag: None

The kinetic theory is useful for

a) determining how much heat   b) explaining how matter and
is necessary to melt a solid.   energy are related.

c) testing the temperature of a d) showing the differences
gas.   between states of matter.

d

16) Item Type: Multiple Choice   Objective: 2-2.1
    Level: 1   Tag: None

The kinetic theory states that the higher the temperature, the faster the

     a) particles that make up a substance move.   b) bonds between atoms break down.

     c) molecules of gas rush together.   d) lighter particles within a substance clump together.

a

17) Item Type: Multiple Choice   Objective: 2-2.2
    Level: 1   Tag: None

The change of a substance from a solid directly to a gas is called

     a) condensation.   b) evaporation.

     c) melting.   d) sublimation.

d

18) Item Type: Multiple Choice   Objective: 2-2.2
    Level: 1   Tag: None

The ability to change or to move matter is referred to as

     a) kinetic theory.   b) energy.

     c) evaporation.   d) heating.

b

19) Item Type: Multiple Choice   Objective: 2-2.2
    Level: 1   Tag: None

All changes of the state of matter require

     a) water.   b) vibration.

     c) energy.   d) sublimation.

c

20) Item Type: Multiple Choice   Objective: 2-2.2
    Level: 1   Tag: None

Evaporation refers to the change of state from a

     a) liquid to a gas.   b) gas to a liquid.

     c) solid to a liquid.   d) liquid to a solid.

a

21) Item Type: Multiple Choice   Objective: 2-2.3
    Level: I   Tag: None

The law of conservation of mass states that mass *cannot* be

a) burned.   b) changed in form.

c) created or destroyed.   d) heated or cooled.

c

22) Item Type: Multiple Choice   Objective: 2-2.3
    Level: I   Tag: None

During a chemical or physical change, energy may be

a) created.   b) destroyed.

c) greatly increased in   d) converted into another form.

d

23) Item Type: Multiple Choice   Objective: 2-2.3
    Level: II   Tag: None

You burn a log of wood, and only a small pile of ashes is left. What has happened?

a) A large amount of mass has   b) A small amount of mass has
been lost.   been converted into a large
                                     amount of heat energy.

c) The total mass of the wood and   d) The total amount of energy
oxygen is the same as the total   is less than before.
mass of the ash and gases.

c

24) Item Type: Multiple Choice   Objective: 2-2.2
    Level: I   Tag: None

A liquid changes rapidly into a gas at the liquid's

a) boiling point.   b) freezing point.

c) melting point.   d) condensation point.

a

25) Item Type: Multiple Choice   Objective: 2-3.1
    Level: I   Tag: None

Knowing the chemical properties of a substance will tell you how the substance

        a) looks.   b) smells.

        c) can be broken down into   d) reacts with other substances.

d

26) Item Type: Multiple Choice   Objective: 2-3.1
    Level: I   Tag: None

Which of the following is *not* an example of a physical property?

        a) freezing point   b) boiling point

        c) reactivity   d) density

c

27) Item Type: Multiple Choice   Objective: 2-3.2
    Level: II   Tag: None

Steel has a density of 7.8 g/cm^3. What is the mass of a block of steel with
a volume of 600 cm^3?

        a) 76.9 g   b) 468 g

        c) 4680 g   d) 7690 g

c

28) Item Type: Multiple Choice   Objective: 2-3.2
    Level: II   Tag: None

Lead has a density of 11.3 g/cm^3. What is the volume of a block of lead with a mass of
282.5 g?

        a) 2.5 cm^3 b) 25 cm^3

        c) 250 cm^3 d) 2500 cm^3

b

24

29) Item Type: Multiple Choice   Objective: 2-3.2
    Level: II   Tag: None

A substance has a mass of 360 g and a volume of 7.5 cm^3. What is its density?

   a) 2700 g/cm^3 b) 270 g/cm^3

   c) 480 g/cm^3 d) 48 g/cm^3

d

30) Item Type: Multiple Choice   Objective: 2-3.3
    Level: I   Tag: None

Which of the following is an example of a chemical change?

   a) ice melting   b) paint fading

   c) pounding gold into a coin   d) a puddle of water
                                       evaporating

b

31) Item Type: Multiple Choice   Objective: 2-3.3
    Level: I   Tag: None

Which of the following is an example of a physical change?

   a) dissolving salt in water   b) burning wood into charcoal

   c) cooking an egg   d) rusting iron

a

32) Item Type: Multiple Choice   Objective: 2-3.5
    Level: I   Tag: None

Ice floats in water because it is

   a) more dense than water.   b) less dense than water.

   c) colder than water.   d) warmer than water.

b

33) Item Type: Multiple Choice   Objective: 2-3.3
    Level: I   Tag: None

Digesting food is an example of

   a) physical change.   b) change of state.

   c) chemical change.   d) buoyancy.

c

34) Item Type: Multiple Choice   Objective: 2-3.4
Level: I   Tag: None

When water is broken down, what happens to the oxygen and hydrogen atoms it is made of?

a) They combine with oxygen in air to produce new substances.

b) They are rearranged to form hydrogen and oxygen gas

c) They are destroyed.

d) They increase in size until they form a solid.

b

35) Item Type: Multiple Choice   Objective: 2-3.3
Level: I   Tag: None

Grinding quartz crystals down to produce sand is an example of a

a) change of state.

b) chemical change.

c) chemical reaction.

d) physical change.

d

36) Item Type: Multiple Choice   Objective: 2-3.3
Level: I   Tag: None

The tendency of a less dense substance to float in a more dense liquid is called

a) viscosity.

b) density.

c) sublimation.

d) buoyancy.

d

37) Item Type: Short Answer   Objective: 2-1.1
Level: I   Tag: None

Sound is *not* made of matter because it has no _____.

mass or volume

38) Item Type: Short Answer   Objective: 2-1.1
Level: I   Tag: None

Aluminum, oxygen, and carbon are examples of _____.

elements

53) Item Type: Short Answer   Objective: 2-2.2
    Level: I   Tag: None

As heat is added to a solid substance, the atoms _____ _____ and move apart.

vibrate faster

54) Item Type: Short Answer   Objective: 2-2.2
    Level: I   Tag: None

When water _____, energy is released.

freezes

55) Item Type: Short Answer   Objective: 2-2.2
    Level: I   Tag: None

For any change of state to occur, _____ must be transferred.

energy

56) Item Type: Short Answer   Objective: 2-2.2
    Level: None   Tag: None

Ice cubes left in the freezer for several months will become smaller because of

_____.

sublimation

57) Item Type: Short Answer   Objective: 2-2.3
    Level: I   Tag: None

Energy may be converted from one form to another, but
it *cannot* be _____ ___ _____.

created or destroyed

58) Item Type: Short Answer   Objective: 2-2.3
    Level: I   Tag: None

When you burn gasoline in a car's engine, you produce energy to move the car plus
energy in the form of _____.

heat

59) Item Type: Short Answer   Objective: 2-2.3
    Level: I   Tag: None

When a piece of paper is burned, the amount of matter before
is _____ _____ _____ the amount of matter afterward.

the same as

Chapter 2

60) Item Type: Short Answer   Objective: 2-2.3
Level: 1   Tag: None

During a chemical or physical change, energy may be _____
from one form to another.

converted

61) Item Type: Short Answer   Objective: 2-3.1
Level: 1   Tag: None

Gold is usually found in a pure form in nature because it is _____.

nonreactive

62) Item Type: Short Answer   Objective: 2-3.1
Level: 1   Tag: None

A _____ property describes how a substance acts when it reacts with other
substances.

chemical

63) Item Type: Short Answer   Objective: 2-3.1
Level: 1   Tag: None

For any pure substance, the boiling point and melting point will always remain

_____.

constant

64) Item Type: Short Answer   Objective: 2-3.2
Level: 1   Tag: None

The density of _____ is 1.0.

water

65) Item Type: Short Answer   Objective: 2-3.2
Level: 1   Tag: None

The _____ of a substance is defined as its mass divided by its volume.

density

66) Item Type: Short Answer   Objective: 2-3.2
Level: 1   Tag: None

Ice floats in water because it is _____ _____ than water.

less dense

30

67) Item Type: Short Answer   Objective: 2-3.3
     Level: I   Tag: None

We inhale oxygen and exhale carbon dioxide as a result of a _____ change
in our bodies.

| chemical |

68) Item Type: Short Answer   Objective: 2-3.3
     Level: I   Tag: None

A chemical change is a change in the _____ of a substance.

| composition |

69) Item Type: Short Answer   Objective: 2-3.3
     Level: II   Tag: None

Grinding wheat into flour is an example of a _____ change.

| physical |

70) Item Type: Short Answer   Objective: 2-3.5
     Level: II   Tag: None

Copper is used to make electric wire because it is a good _____.

| conductor |

71) Item Type: Short Answer   Objective: 2-3.5
     Level: II   Tag: None

Tooth fillings are often made of gold or porcelain because these materials are

_____.

| nonreactive |

72) Item Type: Short Answer   Objective: 2-3.5
     Level: I   Tag: None

Flammability is a chemical property that tells whether a substance reacts
in the presence of _____.

| oxygen |

73) Item Type: Essay   Objective: 2-1.1
     Level: III   Tag: None

How do you know that the air you breathe is matter, even though you can't see it?

| Possible answer: Matter has weight and takes up space. You know that air takes up space, because when you breathe in, your lungs fill with air and expand. |

74) Item Type: Essay   Objective: 2-1.2
    Level: III   Tag: None

Explain the difference among the following three substances: carbon (C), carbon dioxide (CO_2), and oxygen (O_2).

Carbon (C) represents a pure element. Carbon dioxide (CO_2) is a molecule formed by a chemical combination of carbon and oxygen. It is unlike either carbon or oxygen. Oxygen (O_2) is a molecule made up of two like atoms.

75) Item Type: Essay   Objective: 2-1.2
    Level: III   Tag: None

"Carbonated drinks are homogeneous mixtures." Explain this statement.

Carbonated drinks are mixtures of water, sugar, flavorings, and dissolved carbon dioxide gas. They are homogeneous because the mixing occurs between the individual units and is the same throughout.

76) Item Type: Essay   Objective: 2-2.1
    Level: III   Tag: None

You go into a coffee house, and the whole place is filled with the pungent smell. Explain what is happening, according to the kinetic theory.

As a substance is heated, the molecules it is made of move faster and faster. Eventually, some escape in the form of gases, and it is those molecules that reach your nose and cause the rich smell.

77) Item Type: Essay   Objective: 2-2.2
    Level: III   Tag: None

Explain what it means to state that energy is transferred in order for any change of state to occur. Give at least two examples.

Any change of state involves either heating or cooling, which is energy transfer between substances. When water freezes, it releases energy into the surrounding air. When ice melts, it absorbs heat energy.

78) Item Type: Essay   Objective: 2-3.1
    Level: III   Tag: None

Describe the chemical and physical properties of the case that protects your computer. Explain why the materials used were chosen.

Hard plastic: hard, solid at room temperature, nonreactive, smooth, dull in color. Hard and solid to protect the computer; nonreactive to be durable; smooth to be easy to keep clean; dull in color to blend in with surroundings.

79) Item Type: Essay   Objective: 2-3.2
Level: III   Tag: None

Why is density an important property of matter? Explain at least two ways in which density has practical importance.

> Density affects how heavy something is, as well as whether something floats in a particular liquid. Boats float because the air inside the vessel is less dense than the water the vessel sits in. Cream can be separated from milk because it is less dense than milk and floats to the top.

80) Item Type: Essay   Objective: 2-3.2
Level: III   Tag: None

Explain what it means to say that a chemical change is a change in composition. Give an example of a chemical change and state what changes occur.

> In a chemical change, substances react together to produce new substances. For example, rusting of iron is a chemical change. Oxygen in the air reacts with the iron to produce iron oxide, a new substance that is neither iron nor oxygen.

1) Item Type: Multiple Choice   Objective: 3-1.1
    Level: I   Tag: None

Dalton's atomic theory stated that every element was made of atoms that could not be subdivided, atoms of the same element are alike, and

a) atoms are made of protons, neutrons, and electrons.

b) the nucleus is the center of the atom.

c) atoms can join to form molecules.

d) atoms are constantly in motion.

c

2) Item Type: Multiple Choice   Objective: 3-1.1
    Level: I   Tag: None

Dalton's atomic theory was accepted because

a) there was evidence to support it.

b) Democritus said that it was correct.

c) Dalton invented the electron microscope.

d) Dalton showed how molecules are formed.

a

3) Item Type: Multiple Choice   Objective: 3-1.1
    Level: I   Tag: None

Which statement is true according to Dalton's theory?

a) Atoms of different elements can join to form larger atoms.

b) Atoms can be subdivided into smaller particles.

c) Atoms of the same element differ in electric charge.

d) Atoms of the same element are exactly alike.

d

4) Item Type: Multiple Choice   Objective: 3-1.2
    Level: I   Tag: None

Which statement about the atomic nucleus is correct?

a) The nucleus is made of protons and neutrons and has a negative charge.

b) The nucleus is made of protons and neutrons and has a positive charge.

c) The nucleus is made of electrons and has a positive charge.

d) The nucleus is made of electrons and has a negative charge.

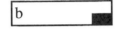

b

5) Item Type: Multiple Choice   Objective: 3-1.2
    Level: I   Tag: None

The charge of an electron is

a) -2

b) -1

c) 0

d) $+1$

b

6) Item Type: Multiple Choice   Objective: 3-1.2
    Level: I   Tag: None

Atoms have no electric charge because they

a) have an equal number of charged and noncharged particles.

b) have neutrons in their nuclei.

c) have an equal number of electrons and protons.

d) have an equal number of neutrons and protons.

c

7) Item Type: Multiple Choice   Objective: 3-1.3
    Level: I   Tag: None

According to Bohr's model of the atom, electrons behave like

a) planets orbiting the sun.

b) waves on a vibrating string.

c) light energy in a vacuum.

d) planets rotating on their axes.

a

8) Item Type: Multiple Choice Objective: 3-1.3
   Level: I Tag: None

According to Bohr's theory, an electron's path around the nucleus defines its

a) electric charge. b) atomic mass.

c) energy level. d) speed.

c

9) Item Type: Multiple Choice Objective: 3-1.3
   Level: I Tag: None

According to modern atomic theory, it is nearly impossible to determine an electron's exact

a) color. b) position.

c) charge d) mass.

b

10) Item Type: Multiple Choice Objective: 3-2.1
    Level: I Tag: None

The order of elements in the periodic table is based on

a) the number of protons in b) the electric charge of the
the nucleus. nucleus.

c) the number of neutrons in d) atomic mass.
the nucleus.

a

11) Item Type: Multiple Choice Objective: 3-2.1
    Level: I Tag: None

Atoms of elements that are in the same group have the same number of

a) protons. b) neutrons.

c) valence electrons. d) protons and neutrons.

c

12) Item Type: Multiple Choice   Objective: 3-2.1
    Level: I   Tag: None

Valence electrons determine an atom's

a) mass.   b) chemical properties.

c) electric charge.   d) period.

b

13) Item Type: Multiple Choice   Objective: 3-2.2
    Level: I   Tag: None

Ionization refers to the process of

a) changing from one period   b) losing or gaining protons.
to another.

c) turning lithium into   d) losing or gaining electrons.
fluorine.

d

14) Item Type: Multiple Choice   Objective: 3-2.2
    Level: I   Tag: None

A lithium ion is much less reactive than a lithium atom because it

a) is much more massive.   b) has a full outermost energy
                                  level.

c) has a negative electric   d) is in a different group in the
charge.   periodic table.

b

15) Item Type: Multiple Choice   Objective: 3-2.3
    Level: II   Tag: None

Oxygen has atomic number 8. This means that an oxygen atom has

a) eight neutrons in its   b) a total of eight protons and
nucleus.   neutrons.

c) eight protons in its nucleus. d) a total of eight neutrons and
                                  electrons.

c

16) Item Type: Multiple Choice   Objective: 3-2.3
    Level: I   Tag: None

An atom's mass number equals the number of

a) protons plus the number of electrons.

b) protons plus the number of neutrons.

c) protons.

d) neutrons.

b

17) Item Type: Multiple Choice   Objective: 3-2.4
    Level: I   Tag: None

Which statement about an element's average atomic mass is correct?

a) It is determined by counting the number of isotopes in a sample of the element.

b) It is equal to one-twelfth the mass of the most common isotope.

c) It is a weighted average, so common isotopes have a greater effect than uncommon ones.

d) It is based on an isotope's charge, so negatively charged isotopes have a greater effect than positive ones.

c

18) Item Type: Multiple Choice   Objective: 3-2.4
    Level: I   Tag: None

An atomic mass unit is equal to

a) one-half the mass of a hydrogen atom.

b) one-fourth the mass of a lithium atom.

c) one-twelfth the mass of a carbon-12 atom.

d) one-fifteenth the mass of a nitrogen-15 atom.

c

19) Item Type: Multiple Choice   Objective: 3-3.1
    Level: I   Tag: None

Which statement about the alkali metals is correct?

a) They are located in the left-most column of the periodic table.

b) They are extremely nonreactive.

c) They are usually gases.

d) They form negative ions with a 1− charge.

a

20) Item Type: Multiple Choice   Objective: 3-3.1
    Level: I   Tag: None

Which of the following elements is an alkali metal?

        a) calcium   b) magnesium

        c) mercury   d) sodium

d

21) Item Type: Multiple Choice   Objective: 3-3.1
    Level: I   Tag: None

Alkali metals are extremely reactive because they

        a) have very small atomic   b) are not solids at room
        masses.   temperature.

        c) have one valence electron   d) have two valence electrons
        that is easily removed to form   that form compounds with
        a positive ion.   calcium and magnesium.

c

22) Item Type: Multiple Choice   Objective: 3-3.2
    Level: I   Tag: None

Which statement about noble gases is correct?

        a) They form compounds with   b) They exist as single atoms
        very bright colors.   rather than as molecules.

        c) They are highly reactive   d) They are extremely rare in
        with both metals and   nature.
        nonmetals.

b

23) Item Type: Multiple Choice   Objective: 3-3.2
    Level: I   Tag: None

Semiconductors are elements that

        a) have large atomic masses   b) do not form compounds.
        but small atomic numbers.

        c) can conduct heat and   d) are extremely hard.
        electricity under certain
        conditions.

c

24) Item Type: Multiple Choice   Objective: 3-3.2
    Level: I   Tag: None

Most halogens form compounds by

    a) gaining an electron to form a negative ion.

    b) losing an electron to form a positive ion.

    c) losing protons.

    d) joining with both calcium and carbon.

a

25) Item Type: Multiple Choice   Objective: 3-3.3
    Level: I   Tag: None

Group 18 noble gases are inert because

    a) they readily form positive ions.

    b) they can have either a positive or a negative charge.

    c) their outermost energy level is missing one electron.

    d) their outermost energy level is full.

d

26) Item Type: Multiple Choice   Objective: 3-3.3
    Level: I   Tag: None

Carbon and other nonmetals are found in which area of the periodic table?

    a) On the left-most side.

    b) On the right side.

    c) In the middle column of the periodic table.

    d) In the bottom rows.

b

27) Item Type: Multiple Choice   Objective: 3-3.3
    Level: I   Tag: None

Transition metals such as copper or tungsten form compounds by

    a) gaining electrons to form negative ions.

    b) losing electrons to form positive ions.

    c) losing neutrons.

    d) changing shape and color at various temperatures.

b

28) Item Type: Multiple Choice   Objective: 3-4.1
    Level: I   Tag: None

A mole is an SI base unit that describes the

a) mass of a substance.   b) amount of a substance.

c) volume of a substance.   d) electric charge of a
                                        substance.

b

29) Item Type: Multiple Choice   Objective: 3-4.1
    Level: I   Tag: None

If the atomic mass of carbon is 12 amu, 1 mole of pure carbon will have a mass of

a) 6 g   b) 6 mol

c) 12 g   d) 12 mol

c

30) Item Type: Multiple Choice   Objective: 3-4.1
    Level: I   Tag: None

Avogadro's constant is defined as the number of particles in

a) one mole of a pure   b) one liter of a pure
   substance.   substance.

c) one gram of a pure   d) one kilogram of a pure
   substance.   substance.

a

31) Item Type: Multiple Choice   Objective: 3-4.1
    Level: I   Tag: None

Molar mass is defined as

a) the number of particles in   b) the SI base unit that
   1 mole of a substance.   describes the amount of a
                                        substance.

c) the amount of a substance   d) the mass in grams of
   necessary to have a positive   1 mole of a substance.
   charge.

d

Chapter 3

32) Item Type: Multiple Choice   Objective: 3-4.2
Level: II   Tag: None

The average atomic mass of potassium is approximately 39 amu. What is the mass of 2.0 mol of potassium?

a) 0.39 g

b) 0.78 g

c) 39 g

d) 78 g

d

33) Item Type: Multiple Choice   Objective: 3-4.2
Level: II   Tag: None

The average atomic mass of the element cesium is approximately 133 amu. What is the mass of 3.00 mol of cesium?

a) 0.133 g

b) 133 g

c) 266 g

d) 399 g

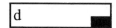
d

34) Item Type: Multiple Choice   Objective: 3-4.3
Level: II   Tag: None

You have 6.50 mol of chromium, which has a molar mass of approximately 52 g/mol. What is the mass in grams of this amount of chromium?

a) 3.38 g

b) 33.8 g

c) 338 g

d) 3.38 kg

c

35) Item Type: Multiple Choice   Objective: 3-4.3
Level: II   Tag: None

What is the mass in grams of 0.75 mol of sulfur, which has a molar mass of approximately 32 g/mol?

a) 16 g

b) 24 g

c) 32 g

d) 240 g

b

Chapter 3

36) Item Type: Multiple Choice   Objective: 3-4.3
    Level: II   Tag: None

You have 85.5 g of fluorine, which has a molar mass of approximately 19 g/mol. How many moles of fluorine do you have?

a) 4.5 mol   b) 19 mol

c) 45 mol   d) 85 mol

a

37) Item Type: Fill-in-the-Blank   Objective: 3-1.1
    Level: I   Tag: None

The word *atom* comes from a Greek word that means "unable to be _____."

divided

38) Item Type: Fill-in-the-Blank   Objective: 3-1.1
    Level: I   Tag: None

The first person who suggested that matter was made up of atoms was the Greek philosopher _____.

Democritus

39) Item Type: Fill-in-the-Blank   Objective: 3-1.1
    Level: I   Tag: None

John Dalton's atomic theory stated that atoms of the same _____ are exactly alike.

element

40) Item Type: Fill-in-the-Blank   Objective: 3-1.2
    Level: I   Tag: None

The nucleus of an atom has a(n) _____ electric charge.

positive

41) Item Type: Fill-in-the-Blank   Objective: 3-1.2
    Level: I   Tag: None

Neutrons and protons are found in the _____ of an atom.

nucleus

42) Item Type: Fill-in-the-Blank   Objective: 3-1.2
    Level: I   Tag: None

Atoms have equal numbers of _____ and _____ .

protons; electrons

43) Item Type: Fill-in-the-Blank   Objective: 3-1.3
    Level: I   Tag: None

Bohr's model of the atom compares electrons to _____ .

planets

44) Item Type: Fill-in-the-Blank   Objective: 3-1.3
    Level: I   Tag: None

According to modern atomic theory, the exact location of a(n) _____ is uncertain.

electron

45) Item Type: Fill-in-the-Blank   Objective: 3-1.3
    Level: I   Tag: None

A region in which there is a high probability of finding an electron is called a(n)

_____ .

orbital

46) Item Type: Fill-in-the-Blank   Objective: 3-2.1
    Level: I   Tag: None

The order of elements in the periodic table is based on the number of _____ in the nucleus.

protons

47) Item Type: Fill-in-the-Blank   Objective: 3-2.1
    Level: I   Tag: None

The _____ states that when elements are listed in order of atomic number, similarities in their properties will emerge in a regular pattern.

periodic law

48) Item Type: Fill-in-the-Blank   Objective: 3-2.1
    Level: I   Tag: None

Because atoms of elements in the same group of the periodic table have the same number of _____ , they have similar properties.

valence electrons

49) Item Type: Fill-in-the-Blank   Objective: 3-2.2
    Level: I   Tag: None

Some elements are highly _____ because their outermost energy levels are only partially filled.

reactive ∎

50) Item Type: Fill-in-the-Blank   Objective: 3-2.2
    Level: I   Tag: None

The valence electron of a lithium atom is easily removed to form a lithium _____ with a charge of 1+.

ion / cation ∎

51) Item Type: Fill-in-the-Blank   Objective: 3-2.3
    Level: I   Tag: None

Isotopes of an element have the same atomic _____ but different atomic _____.

number; masses ∎

52) Item Type: Fill-in-the-Blank   Objective: 3-2.3
    Level: II   Tag: None

An atom of potassium has an atomic mass of 39 amu and an atomic number of 19. It therefore has _____ neutrons in its nucleus.

20 ∎

53) Item Type: Fill-in-the-Blank   Objective: 3-2.3
    Level: I   Tag: None

An element's average atomic mass refers to the weighted average of the masses of all of its naturally occurring _____.

isotopes ∎

54) Item Type: Fill-in-the-Blank   Objective: 3-2.3
    Level: I   Tag: None

_____, the lightest hydrogen isotope, is the most commonly occurring hydrogen isotope.

Protium ∎

55) Item Type: Fill-in-the-Blank   Objective: 3-3.1
    Level: I   Tag: None

Group 1 of the periodic table consists of the _____, a highly reactive
group of elements.

| alkali metals |

56) Item Type: Fill-in-the-Blank   Objective: 3-3.1
    Level: I   Tag: None

Atoms of alkaline-earth metals, such as calcium, have _____ valence electrons.

| two |

57) Item Type: Fill-in-the-Blank   Objective: 3-3.1
    Level: I   Tag: None

The _____ are located in the center of the periodic table.

| transition metals |

58) Item Type: Fill-in-the-Blank   Objective: 3-3.2
    Level: I   Tag: None

The _____ are highly reactive elements located in Group 17 of the periodic table.

| halogens |

59) Item Type: Fill-in-the-Blank   Objective: 3-3.2
    Level: I   Tag: None

Noble gases are nonreactive gaseous elements that are located in Group _____ of the
periodic table.

| 18 |

60) Item Type: Fill-in-the-Blank   Objective: 3-3.2
    Level: I   Tag: None

The most familiar semiconductor, _____, is one of the most abundant elements in
Earth's crust.

| silicon |

61) Item Type: Fill-in-the-Blank   Objective: 3-3.3
    Level: I   Tag: None

Neon is an inert gas because its outer _____ is full of electrons.

| energy level |

62) Item Type: Fill-in-the-Blank   Objective: 3-3.3
    Level: I   Tag: None

Group 17 halogens form compounds by gaining an electron and forming a _____.

negative ion or anion

63) Item Type: Fill-in-the-Blank   Objective: 3-3.3
    Level: I   Tag: None

Nonmetals that can conduct heat and electricity under some circumstances are classified as

_____.

semiconductors

64) Item Type: Fill-in-the-Blank   Objective: 3-4.1
    Level: I   Tag: None

The _____ is the SI unit that is used for counting small particles, such as atoms.

mole

65) Item Type: Fill-in-the-Blank   Objective: 3-4.1
    Level: I   Tag: None

The _____ in _____ of 1 mol of a substance equals its molar mass.

mass; grams

66) Item Type: Fill-in-the-Blank   Objective: 3-4.1
    Level: I   Tag: None

The number of particles in one mole of a substance is referred to as _____.

Avogadro's constant

67) Item Type: Fill-in-the-Blank   Objective: 3-4.2
    Level: II   Tag: None

Use the periodic table to determine the molar mass of the element listed. Round the molar mass to two places to the right of the decimal.

scandium _____ g/mol

44.96

68) Item Type: Fill-in-the-Blank   Objective: 3-4.2
    Level: II   Tag: None

Use the periodic table to determine the molar mass of the element listed. Round the molar mass to two places to the right of the decimal.

zinc _____ g/mol

| 65.39 |

69) Item Type: Fill-in-the-Blank   Objective: 3-4.2
    Level: II   Tag: None

Use the periodic table to determine the molar mass of the element listed. Round the molar mass to two places to the right of the decimal.

phosphorous _____ g/mol

| 30.97 |

70) Item Type: Fill-in-the-Blank   Objective: 3-4.3
    Level: II   Tag: None

The molar mass of krypton is 83.80 g/mol. The mass of 5.00 mol of krypton is _____ g.

| 419 |

71) Item Type: Fill-in-the-Blank   Objective: 3-4.3
    Level: II   Tag: None

The molar mass of nitrogen is 14.01 g/mol. The mass of 0.20 mol of nitrogen is _____ g.

| 2.8 |

72) Item Type: Fill-in-the-Blank   Objective: 3-4.3
    Level: II   Tag: None

The molar mass of palladium is 106.42 g/mol. Therefore, 53.2 g of palladium contains _____ mol.

| 0.500 |

73) Item Type: Essay   Objective: 3-1.3
    Level: III   Tag: None

Explain the major differences between Bohr's model of the atom and the modern model.

Bohr's model views the atom as a miniature solar system, with electrons representing planets and the nucleus representing the sun. According to this model, the position of each electron can be accurately determined at any point in time. In the modern model, the orbiting electrons are like the blades of a rotating fan, which move so quickly that their position at any given time cannot be determined with certainty.

Chapter 3

74) Item Type: Essay   Objective: 3-1.2
    Level: III   Tag: None

Explain why atoms have no electric charge even though they are made up of charged particles.

Atoms have an equal number of protons, which each have a charge of +1, and electrons, which each have a charge of –1. The positive and negative charges cancel.

75) Item Type: Essay   Objective: 3-2.2
    Level: III   Tag: None

What does it mean to say that some elements are reactive and form ions easily whereas others do not?

Some elements are reactive because the outermost energy levels of their atoms are only partially filled. Therefore, these atoms can easily gain or lose electrons to form ions. The atoms of nonreactive elements have filled outermost energy levels.

76) Item Type: Essay   Objective: 3-2.4
    Level: III   Tag: None

Explain how isotopes affect an element's average atomic mass.

Some elements form several isotopes—atoms with different numbers of neutrons and therefore with different atomic masses. An element's average atomic mass is the weighted average of all its isotopes based on their relative abundance in nature.

77) Item Type: Essay   Objective: 3-3.1
    Level: III   Tag: None

Explain how a chemist defines a metal, and explain the difference between metals and nonmetals.

Metals are elements that exist usually as solids and can conduct heat and electricity. Nonmetals may exist as solids, liquids, or gases and do not conduct heat or electricity.

78) Item Type: Essay   Objective: 3-3.3
    Level: III   Tag: None

Relate an element's chemical properties to the arrangement of electrons in its atoms. Give at least two examples.

Whether an atom's outermost energy level is full determines whether it is reactive or nonreactive. For example, alkali metals such as sodium, which have only one valence electron that can be easily removed, are highly reactive. Alkaline-earth metals, such as calcium and magnesium, which have two valence electrons, are still reactive but not as reactive as alkali metals.

49

79) Item Type: Essay   Objective: 3-4.1
     Level: III   Tag: None

Explain the relationship between moles and grams.

Moles are the SI base unit that tells the amount of something. Grams are the SI base unit of mass. One mole of a substance is always equal to its atomic mass in grams. For example, 1 mol of carbon has a mass of 12.01 g.

80) Item Type: Essay   Objective: 3-4.3
     Level: III   Tag: None

If you know an element's molar mass, explain how you can determine the mass of a particular amount of the element.

You multiply the amount of the element in moles by the element's molar mass.

Chapter 4

1) Item Type: Multiple Choice   Objective: 4-1.1
Level: I   Tag: None

The forces that hold different atoms or ions together are

       a) electric currents.   b) chemical bonds.

       c) physical bonds.   d) nuclear forces.

b

2) Item Type: Multiple Choice   Objective: 4-1.1
Level: I   Tag: None

A mixture is different from a compound because each substance in a mixture

       a) retains its own properties.   b) changes its electric charge.

       c) forms an ion.   d) changes from a solid to a liquid.

a

3) Item Type: Multiple Choice   Objective: 4-1.1
Level: I   Tag: None

A compound differs from a mixture because it

       a) always remains frozen even at high temperatures.   b) is formed from two cations.

       c) always contains the same elements in the same proportion.   d) can form only in the presence of heat energy.

c

4) Item Type: Multiple Choice   Objective: 4-1.2
Level: I   Tag: None

Each molecule of hydrochloric acid, HCl, contains one atom of hydrogen and

       a) one atom of chlorine.   b) one atom of oxygen.

       c) two atoms of chlorine.   d) two atoms of oxygen.

a

5) Item Type: Multiple Choice   Objective: 4-1.2
   Level: I   Tag: None

Each molecule of table sugar, $C_{12}H_{22}O_{11}$, contains

a) 0 atoms of carbon.   b) 1 atom of carbon.

c) 6 atoms of carbon.   d) 12 atoms of carbon.

d

6) Item Type: Multiple Choice   Objective: 4-1.3
   Level: I   Tag: None

Which compound is formed from a tight network of oppositely charged ions?

a) sugar, $C_{12}H_{22}O_{11}$ b) quartz, SiO_2

c) water, H_2O d) salt, NaCl

d

7) Item Type: Multiple Choice   Objective: 4-1.4
   Level: I   Tag: None

In which substance do the molecules have the strongest attractions to one another?

a) sugar, a solid   b) hydrogen, a gas

c) sulfuric acid, a liquid   d) water, a liquid

a

8) Item Type: Multiple Choice   Objective: 4-1.4
   Level: I   Tag: None

Gases take up a lot of space because

a) they have weak chemical   b) their molecules have very
bonds.   little attraction for one another.

c) they contain very few   d) they have a small molar
atoms.   mass.

b

Chapter 4

9) Item Type: Multiple Choice   Objective: 4-2.1
   Level: I   Tag: None

Often atoms join so that each atom will have

a) an even number of electrons.

b) an outermost energy level that is full of electrons.

c) an equal number of protons and electrons.

d) more electrons than either protons or neutrons.

b

10) Item Type: Multiple Choice   Objective: 4-2.1
    Level: I   Tag: None

The bonds that hold atoms together behave most like

a) snap-together blocks.

b) glue.

c) rubber cement.

d) flexible springs.

d

11) Item Type: Multiple Choice   Objective: 4-2.1
    Level: I   Tag: None

When two hydrogen atoms bond, the positive nucleus of one atom attracts the

a) negative nucleus of the other atom.

b) positive electron of the other atom.

c) negative electron of the other atom.

d) positive nucleus of the other atom.

c

12) Item Type: Multiple Choice   Objective: 4-2.2
    Level: I   Tag: None

An ionic bond is a bond that forms between

a) ions with opposite charges.

b) atoms with neutral charges.

c) one atom's nucleus and another atom's electrons.

d) the electrons of two different atoms.

a

13) Item Type: Multiple Choice   Objective: 4-2.2
    Level: I   Tag: None

Covalent bonds are formed between

    a) ions.   b) metal atoms.

    c) nonmetal atoms.   d) compounds.

c

14) Item Type: Multiple Choice   Objective: 4-2.3
    Level: I   Tag: None

In a metallic bond, the nucleus of one atom is attracted by a nearby atom's

    a) nucleus.   b) negative ion.

    c) energy structure.   d) electrons.

d

15) Item Type: Multiple Choice   Objective: 4-2.3
    Level: I   Tag: None

Copper is a good conductor of electricity because its electrons

    a) are positively charged.   b) are free to move from atom
                                     to atom.

    c) can take on either positive   d) are shared between
    or negative charges.   neighboring compounds.

b

16) Item Type: Multiple Choice   Objective: 4-2.4
    Level: I   Tag: None

Solid ionic compounds have very high melting points because they

    a) are positively charged.   b) contain metallic elements.

    c) are made of elements that   d) contain charged ions that are
    are solid at room temperature.   locked tightly together.

d

54

17) Item Type: Multiple Choice   Objective: 4-2.4
     Level: I   Tag: None

In which type of bond do atoms share electrons?

         a) covalent bonds   b) metallic bonds

         c) ionic bonds   d) polyatomic bonds

a

18) Item Type: Multiple Choice   Objective: 4-3.1
     Level: I   Tag: None

The anion formed from an oxygen atom is called a(n)

         a) oxygen ion.   b) oxide ion.

         c) carbon dioxide.   d) nitrous oxide.

b

19) Item Type: Multiple Choice   Objective: 4-3.1
     Level: II   Tag: None

The name *dinitrogen tetroxide* tells you that this compound contains

         a) two nitrogen atoms and   b) four nitrogen atoms and two
         two oxygen atoms.   oxygen atoms.

         c) two nitrogen atoms and   d) four nitrogen atoms and
         four oxygen atoms.   four oxygen atoms.

c

20) Item Type: Multiple Choice   Objective: 4-3.2
     Level: II   Tag: None

Fe_2O_3 is named *iron(III) oxide* because it contains

         a) three oxygen atoms.   b) Fe^{3+} ions.

         c) three iron atoms.   d) O^{3+} ions.

b

21) Item Type: Multiple Choice   Objective: 4-3.1
    Level: II   Tag: None

When copper combines with oxygen to form copper(II) oxide, the charge of the copper ion is

a) Cu^{1+}.   b) Cu^{2+}.

c) Cu^{3+}.   d) Cu^{4+}.

b

22) Item Type: Multiple Choice   Objective: 4-3.2
    Level: II   Tag: None

When nickel combines with fluorine to form nickel(III) fluoride, the charge of the nickel ion is

a) Ni^{1+}.   b) Ni^{2+}.

c) Ni^{3+}.   d) Ni^{4+}.

c

23) Item Type: Multiple Choice   Objective: 4-3.3
    Level: II   Tag: None

The name for the compound with the formula $CuBr_2$ would be written as

a) copper(II) bromide.   b) copper(I) bromide.

c) copper bromine.   d) copper(III) bromide.

a

24) Item Type: Multiple Choice   Objective: 4-3.3
    Level: II   Tag: None

The name for the compound with the formula Cr_2O_3 would be written as

a) chromium(I) oxide.   b) chromium(II) oxide.

c) chromium oxygen.   d) chromium(III) oxide.

d

25) Item Type: Multiple Choice   Objective: 4-3.3
     Level: II   Tag: None

It is possible for different covalent compounds to have the same empirical formula because empirical formulas represent

         a) a total of all ionic bonds.   b) only the cations in the compound.

         c) a model of the compound.   d) a ratio of atoms in the compound.

d

26) Item Type: Multiple Choice   Objective: 4-3.3
     Level: II   Tag: None

Formaldehyde, CH_2O, and acetic acid, $C_2H_4O_2$, have the same empirical formula but different

         a) kinds of cations.   b) kinds of anions.

         c) kinds of atoms.   d) molecular formulas.

d

27) Item Type: Multiple Choice   Objective: 4-4.1
     Level: II   Tag: None

A carbon atom can bond to four other atoms because it has

         a) four different cations.   b) four valence electrons.

         c) two inner energy levels.   d) no protons in its nucleus.

b

28) Item Type: Multiple Choice   Objective: 4-4.1
     Level: I   Tag: None

The simplest organic compound is

         a) aspirin.   b) table sugar.

         c) salt.   d) methane.

d

29) Item Type: Multiple Choice   Objective: 4-4.1
    Level: I   Tag: None

Alkanes are hydocarbons that contain

       a) single covalent bonds only.   b) single or double covalent bonds.

       c) carbon and oxygen only.   d) carbon, hydrogen, and oxygen.

a

30) Item Type: Multiple Choice   Objective: 4-4.2
    Level: I   Tag: None

Alcohols are organic compounds that contain

       a) carbon and oxygen only.   b) carbon and hydrogen only.

       c) carbon, oxygen, and   d) carbon, nitrogen, and
       hydrogen.   hydrogen.

c

31) Item Type: Multiple Choice   Objective: 4-4.2
    Level: I   Tag: None

Polymers are large organic molecules that are made of

       a) cations.   b) anions.

       c) carbon and oxygen only.   d) repeating units.

d

32) Item Type: Multiple Choice   Objective: 4-4.2
    Level: I   Tag: None

Which compounds have carbon-carbon double bonds?

       a) alkanes   b) alkenes

       c) alcohols   d) ionic compounds

b

33) Item Type: Multiple Choice   Objective: 4-4.3
    Level: I   Tag: None

A protein is a polymer that is made of

         a) simple sugars.   b) nitrogen and carbon dioxide.

         c) amino acids.   d) DNA.

c

34) Item Type: Multiple Choice   Objective: 4-4.3
    Level: I   Tag: None

The "rungs" of the DNA "ladder" are made up of

         a) paired monomers.   b) sugar molecules.

         c) phosphates.   d) amino acids.

a

35) Item Type: Multiple Choice   Objective: 4-4.3
    Level: I   Tag: None

Some polymers are elastic because they are made of

         a) carbon.   b) phosphate ladders.

         c) sugar and alcohol.   d) cross-linked chains.

d

36) Item Type: Fill-in-the-Blank   Objective: 4-4.1
    Level: I   Tag: None

When elements combine to form a(n) _____, the resulting properties may be very different from those of the elements that make it.

compound

37) Item Type: Fill-in-the-Blank   Objective: 4-1.1
    Level: I   Tag: None

Unlike a mixture, a compound has a(n) _____ that is always the same.

chemical formula

Chapter 4

38) Item Type: Fill-in-the-Blank   Objective: 4-1.1
    Level: I   Tag: None

The arrangement of _____ or _____ within a substance is its chemical structure.

| atoms; ions |

39) Item Type: Fill-in-the-Blank   Objective: 4-1.2
    Level: I   Tag: None

The chemical formula H_2O means a water molecule contains one _____ for every two _____.

| oxygen atom; hydrogen atoms |

40) Item Type: Fill-in-the-Blank   Objective: 4-1.3
    Level: I   Tag: None

Formula units of salt, NaCl, contain equal numbers of _____ and _____.

| sodium ions; chloride ions |

41) Item Type: Fill-in-the-Blank   Objective: 4-1.3
    Level: I   Tag: None

The distance between the nuclei of two bonded atoms is referred to as _____.

| bond length |

42) Item Type: Fill-in-the-Blank   Objective: 4-1.3
    Level: I   Tag: None

The structural formula for a water molecule is _____.

43) Item Type: Fill-in-the-Blank   Objective: 4-1.4
    Level: I   Tag: None

The melting and boiling points of quartz are very high because of the compound's _____.

| network structure / structure |

44) Item Type: Fill-in-the-Blank   Objective: 4-1.4
    Level: I   Tag: None

Networks can be made of bonded _____ or _____.

| atoms; ions |

45) Item Type: Fill-in-the-Blank   Objective: 4-2.1
    Level: I   Tag: None

Atoms bond in compounds when their _____ interact.

| valence electrons |

46) Item Type: Fill-in-the-Blank   Objective: 4-2.1
    Level: I   Tag: None

In ionic compounds, the positively charged ions are formed from _____ elements.

| metal |

47) Item Type: Fill-in-the-Blank   Objective: 4-2.1
    Level: I   Tag: None

When atoms form bonds and fill their outermost energy levels, they have an electronic arrangement similar to that of a(n) _____.

| noble gas |

48) Item Type: Fill-in-the-Blank   Objective: 4-2.2
    Level: I   Tag: None

The structure of silicon dioxide consists of a _____ of atoms.

| network |

49) Item Type: Fill-in-the-Blank   Objective: 4-2.2
    Level: I   Tag: None

When two chlorine atoms bond, they _____ a pair of electrons.

| share |

50) Item Type: Fill-in-the-Blank   Objective: 4-2.3
    Level: I   Tag: None

A(n) _____ bond is formed by the attraction between positively charged metal ions and the _____ around them.

| metallic; electrons |

51) Item Type: Fill-in-the-Blank   Objective: 4-2.3
    Level: I   Tag: None

A(n) _____ bond is formed when atoms share _____ of electrons.

> covalent; pairs

52) Item Type: Fill-in-the-Blank   Objective: 4-2.4
    Level: I   Tag: None

Most covalent compounds have relatively _____ melting points.

> low

53) Item Type: Fill-in-the-Blank   Objective: 4-2.4
    Level: I   Tag: None

Because polyatomic ions are made of covalently bonded atoms that have either gained or lost electrons, they behave like simple _____.

> ions

54) Item Type: Fill-in-the-Blank   Objective: 4-3.1
    Level: II   Tag: None

A compound whose molecules contain one boron atom and three fluorine atoms would be named _____.

> boron trifluoride

55) Item Type: Fill-in-the-Blank   Objective: 4-3.2
    Level: II   Tag: None

A compound consisting of Br^- and Cd^{2+} ions would be named _____.

> cadmium(II) bromide

56) Item Type: Fill-in-the-Blank   Objective: 4-3.1
    Level: II   Tag: None

A compound consisting of Cr^{3+} ions and OH^- ions would be named _____.

> chromium(III) hydroxide

57) Item Type: Fill-in-the-Blank   Objective: 4-3.2
    Level: II   Tag: None

The charge of each titanium ion in the ionic compound TiO_2 is _____.

> Ti^{4+}

Chapter 4

58) Item Type: Fill-in-the-Blank   Objective: 4-3.2
    Level: II   Tag: None

The charge of each iron ion in the ionic compound FeS is _____.

Fe^{2+}

59) Item Type: Fill-in-the-Blank   Objective: 4-3.3
    Level: II   Tag: None

The chemical formula for the ionic compound consisting of oxide ions and nickel(III) ions is _____.

Ni_2O_3

60) Item Type: Fill-in-the-Blank   Objective: 4-3.3
    Level: II   Tag: None

The chemical formula for the ionic compound consisting of nitride ions and titanium(III) ions is _____.

TiN

61) Item Type: Fill-in-the-Blank   Objective: 4-3.4
    Level: I   Tag: None

The simplest formula for a covalent compound is its _____ formula.

empirical

62) Item Type: Fill-in-the-Blank   Objective: 4-3.4
    Level: I   Tag: None

A compound's _____ formula tells you how many atoms of each type are in one molecule.

molecular

63) Item Type: Fill-in-the-Blank   Objective: 4-4.1
    Level: I   Tag: None

Each carbon atom can form a total of _____ bonds.

four

64) Item Type: Fill-in-the-Blank   Objective: 4-4.1
    Level: I   Tag: None

In addition to carbon, organic compounds almost always contain _____.

hydrogen

65) Item Type: Fill-in-the-Blank   Objective: 4-4.1
    Level: I   Tag: None

When a compound is made of only carbon and hydrogen atoms it is called a(n)

_____.

hydrocarbon

66) Item Type: Fill-in-the-Blank   Objective: 4-4.2
    Level: I   Tag: None

Simple organic compounds that contain a hydroxyl group, −OH, are called _____.

alcohols

67) Item Type: Fill-in-the-Blank   Objective: 4-4.2
    Level: I   Tag: None

_____ are compounds that have repeating subunits.

Polymers

68) Item Type: Fill-in-the-Blank   Objective: 4-4.3
    Level: I   Tag: None

Organic compounds with carbon-carbon double bonds are referred to as _____.

alkenes

69) Item Type: Fill-in-the-Blank   Objective: 4-4.3
    Level: I   Tag: None

Both starches and sugars are made of the elements _____, _____, and

_____.

carbon, hydrogen, oxygen

70) Item Type: Fill-in-the-Blank   Objective: 4-4.3
    Level: I   Tag: None

A(n) _____ is a polymer made of bonded amino acids.

protein

71) Item Type: Fill-in-the-Blank   Objective: 4-4.3
    Level: I   Tag: None

DNA can _____ itself because it is made of two strands that can be separated.

copy / replicate

72) Item Type: Essay   Objective: 4-1.4
      Level: III   Tag: None

Describe how the chemical structure of a compound affects its properties by giving at least two examples.

> Quartz, silicon dioxide, is made of silicon and oxygen atoms bonded together in a strong network structure, making it rigid and giving it a high boiling and a high melting point. Similarly, the ions in solid ionic compounds are locked into rigid structures, causing their melting points to be very high.

73) Item Type: Essay   Objective: 4-1.1
      Level: III   Tag: None

Explain what chemical bonds are and how they hold substances together.

> Chemical bonds are attractive forces that hold substances together. Chemical bonds result when atoms either exchange or share electrons to complete their outermost energy levels. Chemical bonds hold a substance together because the substance is more chemically stable than the atoms or ions that make it up.

74) Item Type: Essay   Objective: 4-2.1
      Level: III   Tag: None

Describe how ionic, covalent, and metallic bonds differ from each other.

> Ionic bonds are formed by the transfer of electrons between two atoms. Covalent bonds are formed when atoms share electrons. Metallic bonds form between metal atoms.

75) Item Type: Essay   Objective: 4-2.1
      Level: III   Tag: None

How does the type of chemical bonds present in a substance affect the substance's properties? Give at least two examples.

> A substance with metallic bonds can conduct electricity because electrons can move freely between metal atoms. Ionic compounds consist of strongly bonded ions and therefore have high melting points.

76) Item Type: Essay   Objective: 4-3.3
      Level: III   Tag: None

When titanium bonds with oxygen, the ionic compound that forms has the chemical formula Ti_2O_3 and consists of Ti^{3+} ions and O^{2-} ions. Explain why the compound has this chemical formula.

> The compound has this chemical formula so that the charges of its ions cancel. Each oxide ion has a charge of 2−, so three oxide ions have a charge of 6−. If there are two titanium(III) ions for every three oxide ions, then the 6+ charge of the titanium ions cancels the 6− charge of the oxide ions to give a neutral compound.

Chapter 4

77) Item Type: Essay   Objective: 4-3.2
     Level: III   Tag: None

What is the difference between the compounds Fe_2O_3 and FeO? Why are they not both called simply iron oxide?

> These are compounds containing two different iron ions, iron(II) ion and iron(III) ion. So although they are both compounds containing iron ions and oxide ions, they have different structures and different properties.

78) Item Type: Essay   Objective: 4-4.3
     Level: III   Tag: None

"Organic compounds are the basis for all life." Explain this statement.

> Organic compounds are carbon-based compounds such as sugars, starches, alcohols, and proteins. Our bodies are made of different proteins, and sugars give us energy. Our DNA is also a type of organic compound called a polymer.

79) Item Type: Essay   Objective: 4-4.1
     Level: III   Tag: None

Why does carbon form the basis for so many different kinds of compounds?

> Carbon atoms can form covalent bonds with four different atoms at one time. This makes it possible for many different compounds to form.

Chapter 5

1) Item Type: Multiple Choice   Objective: 5-1.1
    Level: I   Tag: None

A change in color, such as rusting of metal, is a sign that

      a) a chemical change is taking place.   b) a physical change has just occurred.

      c) oxygen is present.   d) organic chemicals are present.

a

2) Item Type: Multiple Choice   Objective: 5-1.2
    Level: I   Tag: None

A substance that undergoes a change in a chemical reaction is

      a) a product.   b) a chemical.

      c) a reactant.   d) an enzyme.

c

3) Item Type: Multiple Choice   Objective: 5-1.2
    Level: I   Tag: None

What happens in a chemical reaction?

      a) Atoms are destroyed.   b) Atoms are created.

      c) Atoms are heated and cooled.   d) Atoms are rearranged.

d

4) Item Type: Multiple Choice   Objective: 5-1.3
    Level: I   Tag: None

In an exothermic reaction, energy is transferred from

      a) the reactants to the surroundings.   b) the surroundings to the reactants.

      c) one reactant to another.   d) the container to the chemicals.

a

Chapter 5

5)   Item Type: Multiple Choice   Objective: 5-1.3
     Level: I   Tag: None

Which statement about endothermic reactions is correct?

a) Energy is always created in   b) Energy is transferred from the
the form of heat.   surroundings to the reactants.

c) Energy is used to force   d) Energy is transferred from the
electrons to move to higher   reactants to the surroundings.
energy levels.

b

6)   Item Type: Multiple Choice   Objective: 5-1.4
     Level: I   Tag: None

Chemical energy is energy that is

a) added to a reaction in the   b) present within atoms and
form of heat.   molecules.

c) caused by the movement of   d) released only when oxygen
electricity.   is present.

b

7)   Item Type: Multiple Choice   Objective: 5-1.4
     Level: I   Tag: None

The energy source in photosynthesis is

a) light energy.   b) chemical energy.

c) heat energy.   d) kinetic energy.

a

8)   Item Type: Multiple Choice   Objective: 5-1.4
     Level: I   Tag: None

Most of the energy in an isooctane reaction is released in the form of

a) heat and light.   b) electrical energy.

c) water.   d) sound.

a

9) Item Type: Multiple Choice   Objective: 5-2.1
Level: I   Tag: None

A synthesis reaction is a reaction between at least two compounds in which

    a) one breaks down into at least two products.

    b) a compound is decomposed by an electric current.

    c) a compound burns in the presence of oxygen.

    d) a new, more complex compound is formed.

d

10) Item Type: Multiple Choice   Objective: 5-2.1
Level: I   Tag: None

What kind of reaction occurs when potassium is placed in water?

    a) a single-displacement reaction

    b) a double-displacement reaction

    c) a decomposition reaction

    d) electrolysis

a

11) Item Type: Multiple Choice   Objective: 5-2.1
Level: I   Tag: None

Which of the following is an example of a decomposition reaction?

    a) photosynthesis

    b) digestion

    c) respiration

    d) exchange of ions between two compounds

b

12) Item Type: Multiple Choice   Objective: 5-2.2
Level: I   Tag: None

The product of the synthesis reaction between sodium and chlorine gas is

    a) polyethylene.

    b) carbon dioxide.

    c) sodium chloride.

    d) copper (II) chloride.

c

13) Item Type: Multiple Choice   Objective: 5-2.2
    Level: I   Tag: None

    When methane reacts with abundant amounts of oxygen, the products are

            a) carbon dioxide and water.   b) carbon monoxide and water.

            c) soot and water.   d) simple sugar and oxygen.

    a

14) Item Type: Multiple Choice   Objective: 5-2.2
    Level: I   Tag: None

    When water is broken down by electrolysis, the products are

            a) water and carbon dioxide.   b) hydrogen and oxygen ions.

            c) hydrogen gas and oxygen gas.   d) oxygen and methane.

    c

15) Item Type: Multiple Choice   Objective: 5-2.3
    Level: I   Tag: None

    Fragments of molecules that have at least one electron available for bonding are called

            a) ions.   b) orbits.

            c) protons.   d) radicals.

    d

16) Item Type: Multiple Choice   Objective: 5-2.3
    Level: I   Tag: None

    In a redox reaction, the substance that accepts electrons is said to be

            a) reduced.   b) oxidized.

            c) electrified.   d) clarified.

    a

17) Item Type: Multiple Choice   Objective: 5-2.3
    Level: I   Tag: None

    When iron reacts with oxygen to form rust, each iron atom

            a) loses three ions.   b) loses three electrons.

            c) gains three ions.   d) gains three electrons.

    b

18) Item Type: Multiple Choice   Objective: 5-3.1
    Level: I   Tag: None

A chemical equation is balanced by changing or adding

   a) chemical symbols.   b) subscripts.

   c) coefficients.   d) reactants.

c

19) Item Type: Multiple Choice   Objective: 5-3.1
    Level: I   Tag: None

A balanced chemical equation shows the proportions of reactants and products necessary for

   a) the reaction to occur.   b) mass to be conserved.

   c) energy use to be minimized.   d) electrolysis to occur.

b

20) Item Type: Multiple Choice   Objective: 5-3.2
    Level: II   Tag: None

In the reaction $2H_2O \rightarrow 2H_2 + O_2$, if you start with 2 mol of water, how many moles of hydrogen gas are produced?

   a) 1 mol   b) 2 mol

   c) 3 mol   d) 4 mol

b

21) Item Type: Multiple Choice   Objective: 5-3.4
    Level: II   Tag: None

In the reaction $2H_2O_2 \rightarrow 2H_2O + O_2$, if you start with 4 mol of H_2O_2, how many moles of O_2 will you end up with?

   a) 4 mol   b) 3 mol

   c) 2 mol   d) 1 mol

c

22) Item Type: Multiple Choice   Objective: 5-3.4
     Level: II   Tag: None

If you start with 5 mol of O_2 in the reaction $2Mg + O_2 \rightarrow 2MgO$, how many moles of Mg will you need?

         a) 4 mol   b) 5 mol

         c) 8 mol   d) 10 mol

d

23) Item Type: Multiple Choice   Objective: 5-3.3
     Level: I   Tag: None

In the reaction $H_2S + 2O_2 \rightarrow H_2SO_4$, the law of definite proportions predicts that for every mole of H_2S you will need how many moles of O_2?

         a) 1 mol   b) 2 mol

         c) 3 mol   d) 4 mol

b

24) Item Type: Multiple Choice   Objective: None
     Level: II   Tag: None

In the reaction $2Mg + O_2 \rightarrow 2MgO$, the law of definite proportions states that for every 2 moles of Mg you will need how many moles of O_2?

         a) 1 mol   b) 2 mol

         c) 3 mol   d) 4 mol

a

25) Item Type: Multiple Choice   Objective: 5-3.5
     Level: II   Tag: None

In a balanced chemical reaction, the total mass of the products always equals the

         a) molar mass of the reactants.   b) atomic mass of the reactants.

         c) total mass of the reactants.   d) proportional masses of the reactants.

c

Chapter 5

26) Item Type: Multiple Choice   Objective: 5-3.5
    Level: II   Tag: None

A balanced chemical equation indicates both the number of particles of reactants and products and the number of

        a) orbits.   b) electrons.

        c) nuclei.   d) moles.

d

27) Item Type: Multiple Choice   Objective: 5-4.1
    Level: II   Tag: None

All of the following factors may speed up a chemical reaction *except*

        a) smaller surface area.   b) higher pressure.

        c) higher temperature.   d) presence of a catalyst.

a

28) Item Type: Multiple Choice   Objective: 5-4.1
    Level: II   Tag: None

Large, bulky molecules react more slowly than small ones because they have less opportunity to

        a) become heated.   b) be mixed with catalysts.

        c) collide with other molecules.   d) increase their surface area.

c

29) Item Type: Multiple Choice   Objective: 5-4.1
    Level: II   Tag: None

What could you do to make yeast dough rise more slowly?

        a) Add more yeast to the mixture.   b) Knead the dough more vigorously.

        c) Add mold spores to the dough.   d) Reduce the temperature.

d

Chapter 5

30) Item Type: Multiple Choice   Objective: 5-4.2
    Level: II   Tag: None

An enzyme is a special kind of catalyst that works to

a) speed up a specific   b) break down chemical
biochemical reaction.   elements.

c) provide a special place   d) maintain the correct
where reactants can collect   temperature for a reaction.
and interact.

a

31) Item Type: Multiple Choice   Objective: 5-4.2
    Level: II   Tag: None

Which enzyme breaks down cellulose into smaller molecules?

a) amylase   b) cellulase

c) protease   d) lipase

b

32) Item Type: Multiple Choice   Objective: 5-4.3
    Level: I   Tag: None

When a chemical reaction and its reverse are occurring at the same time and at the same
rate, the reaction has achieved

a) displacement.   b) equilibrium.

c) imbalance.   d) decomposition.

b

33) Item Type: Multiple Choice   Objective: 5-4.3
    Level: I   Tag: None

What is the relationship between chemical equilibrium and the rates of forward and reverse
reaction?

a) In equilibrium, the forward   b) In equilibrium, the forward
reaction rate must be greater   reaction rate must be less than
than the reverse reaction rate. the reverse reaction rate.

c) In equilibrium, the forward   d) In equilibrium, both forward
and reverse reaction rates   and reverse reactions must
must be equal.   stop.

c

34) Item Type: Multiple Choice   Objective: 5-4.4
Level: I   Tag: None

Le Chatelier's principle states that increasing temperature favors a reaction that

    a) releases energy as heat.   b) requires energy as heat.

    c) involves a chemical catalyst.   d) involves an enzyme.

b

35) Item Type: Multiple Choice   Objective: 5-4.4
Level: I   Tag: None

Increasing the concentration of one substance in an equilibrium reaction favors the reaction that

    a) absorbs energy as heat.   b) releases energy as heat.

    c) produces less of that substance.   d) produces more of that substance.

c

36) Item Type: Fill-in-the-Blank   Objective: 5-1.1
Level: I   Tag: None

When bread rises, this is a sign that a chemical reaction is producing _____.

carbon dioxide gas

37) Item Type: Fill-in-the-Blank   Objective: 5-1.1
Level: I   Tag: None

A change of _____ is a sign that a chemical reaction is taking place.

color

38) Item Type: Fill-in-the-Blank   Objective: 5-1.1
Level: I   Tag: None

A sign that a chemical reaction is taking place is release of energy in the form of _____ or _____.

light; heat

39) Item Type: Fill-in-the-Blank   Objective: 5-1.2
Level: I   Tag: None

The changes that are visible during a chemical reaction are signs that the _____ in the reactants have been rearranged.

atoms

Chapter 5

40) Item Type: Fill-in-the-Blank   Objective: 5-1.3
    Level: I   Tag: None

In a chemical reaction, atoms are _____, but they are not created or destroyed.

rearranged

41) Item Type: Fill-in-the-Blank   Objective: 5-1.3
    Level: I   Tag: None

A chemical reaction that transfers energy from the reactants to the surroundings is referred to as _____.

exothermic

42) Item Type: Fill-in-the-Blank   Objective: 5-1.3
    Level: I   Tag: None

A(n) _____ reaction is one in which heat is transferred from the surroundings to the reactants.

endothermic

43) Item Type: Fill-in-the-Blank   Objective: 5-1.4
    Level: I   Tag: None

Photosynthesis is an example of a(n) _____ chemical reaction in which plants use sunlight to make glucose and oxygen.

endothermic

44) Item Type: Fill-in-the-Blank   Objective: 5-1.4
    Level: I   Tag: None

_____ is an exothermic reaction in which living things produce light.

Bioluminescence

45) Item Type: Fill-in-the-Blank   Objective: 5-2.1
    Level: I   Tag: None

The general formula for a synthesis reaction is _____.

$A + B \rightarrow AB$

46) Item Type: Fill-in-the-Blank   Objective: 5-2.1
    Level: I   Tag: None

In a(n) _____ reaction, the reactants are broken down into other substances.

decomposition

Chapter 5

47) Item Type: Fill-in-the-Blank   Objective: 5-2.1
    Level: I   Tag: None

In a combustion reaction, _____ is used to make reactants burn.

| oxygen |

48) Item Type: Fill-in-the-Blank   Objective: 5-2.2
    Level: I   Tag: None

When methane burns in the presence of insufficient oxygen, the products of the reaction
are water and _____.

| carbon monoxide (OR soot) |

49) Item Type: Fill-in-the-Blank   Objective: 5-2.2
    Level: I   Tag: None

Alkali metals react violently with water to form metal ions, hydroxide ions, and

_____.

| hydrogen gas (or H_2) |

50) Item Type: Fill-in-the-Blank   Objective: 5-2.2
    Level: I   Tag: None

Aluminum undergoes a single-displacement reaction with copper (II) sulfate to form
aluminum sulfate and _____.

| copper |

51) Item Type: Fill-in-the-Blank   Objective: 5-2.3
    Level: I   Tag: None

A substance is said to be _____ when it gains electrons.

| reduced |

52) Item Type: Fill-in-the-Blank   Objective: 5-2.3
    Level: I   Tag: None

Radicals react quickly to form covalent bonds with nearby substances because they have
_____ available for bonding.

| electrons |

53) Item Type: Fill-in-the-Blank   Objective: 5-2.3
    Level: I   Tag: None

A reaction that involves the transfer of _____ is called a(n) _____ reaction.

| electrons; redox OR reduction/oxidation |

54) Item Type: Fill-in-the-Blank Objective: 5-3.1
Level: II Tag: None

Balance the following chemical equation by filling in the correct coefficient on the right-hand side. $H_2 + Cl_2 \rightarrow$ _____ HCl

2

55) Item Type: Fill-in-the-Blank Objective: 5-3.1
Level: II Tag: None

Balance the following chemical equation by filling in the correct coefficients.

_____KI + $Br_2 \rightarrow$ _____KBr + I_2

2; 2

56) Item Type: Fill-in-the-Blank Objective: 5-3.2
Level: II Tag: None

Suppose you were producing zinc chloride by the reaction $Zn + 2HCl \rightarrow ZnCl_2 + H_2$. If you started with 4 moles of zinc, you would need _____ moles of hydrogen chloride and you would produce _____ moles of zinc chloride.

8; 4

57) Item Type: Fill-in-the-Blank Objective: 5-3.2
Level: II Tag: None

In the chemical equation $CH_4 + O_2 \rightarrow CO_2 + 2H_2O$, for every one mole of carbon dioxide you produced, you would have _____ mole/moles of water.

2

58) Item Type: Fill-in-the-Blank Objective: 5-3.3
Level: I Tag: None

The law of definite proportions states that a compound always contains the same _____ in the same _____.

elements; proportions

59) Item Type: Fill-in-the-Blank Objective: 5-3.3
Level: II Tag: None

You are producing magnesium oxide by the reaction $2Mg + O_2 \rightarrow 2MgO$. If you start out with 6 moles of magnesium, you will need _____ moles of oxygen, and you will produce _____ moles of magnesium oxide.

3; 6

Chapter 5

60) Item Type: Fill-in-the-Blank   Objective: 5-3.4
    Level: II   Tag: None

In the chemical equation $H_2 + Cl_2 \rightarrow 2HCl$, the mole ratios are _____.

| 1:1:2 | ■ |

61) Item Type: Fill-in-the-Blank   Objective: 5-3.4
    Level: II   Tag: None

In the chemical equation $FeS + 2HCl \rightarrow FeCl_2 + H_2S$, the mole ratios are _____.

| 1:2:1:1 | ■ |

62) Item Type: Fill-in-the-Blank   Objective: 5-3.5
    Level: I   Tag: None

In a chemical reaction, the combined molar masses of the _____ equals the combined molar masses of the _____.

| reactants; products | ■ |

63) Item Type: Fill-in-the-Blank   Objective: 5-4.1
    Level: I   Tag: None

If you _____ the temperature of a reaction, generally you will _____ the rate of the reaction.

| increase; increase or decrease; decrease | ■ |

64) Item Type: Fill-in-the-Blank   Objective: 5-4.1
    Level: I   Tag: None

If you _____ the surface area of a reactant, you will probably _____ the rate of the reaction.

| increase; increase or decrease; decrease | ■ |

65) Item Type: Fill-in-the-Blank   Objective: 5-4.1
    Level: I   Tag: None

Increasing the _____ or _____ at which a reaction occurs usually increases the rate of reaction.

| temperature; pressure | ■ |

66) Item Type: Fill-in-the-Blank   Objective: 5-4.2
    Level: I   Tag: None

A catalyst that slows a reaction is called a(n) _____.

| inhibitor | ■ |

67) Item Type: Fill-in-the-Blank   Objective: 5-4.2
    Level: I   Tag: None

An enzyme is a(n) _____ that acts as a(n) _____ in a chemical reaction that takes place in a living thing.

| protein; catalyst |

68) Item Type: Fill-in-the-Blank   Objective: 5-4.3
    Level: I   Tag: None

In a state of equilibrium, a reaction and its reverse occur at the same _____ and at the same _____.

| time; rate |

69) Item Type: Fill-in-the-Blank   Objective: 5-4.3
    Level: I   Tag: None

Equilibrium is achieved when the _____ and _____ reactions continue to take place at the same rate.

| forward; reverse |

70) Item Type: Fill-in-the-Blank   Objective: 5-4.4
    Level: I   Tag: None

When a reaction is at equilibrium, increasing the pressure favors the reaction that produces _____.

| less gas |

71) Item Type: Fill-in-the-Blank   Objective: 5-4.4
    Level: I   Tag: None

When a reaction is at equilibrium, increasing the temperature favors the reaction that _____.

| absorbs energy as heat |

72) Item Type: Essay   Objective: 5-1.1
    Level: III   Tag: None

Explain why energy is necessary to chemical reactions, and describe some common sources of energy.

| Energy is necessary to break the bonds that hold molecules together, so that the atoms can recombine and form other molecules. Energy may come from the sun, as added heat, or from the energy stored within the atoms and molecules themselves. |

Chapter 5

73) Item Type: Essay   Objective: 5-1.3
     Level: III   Tag: None

"Photosynthesis, the basis for all life on Earth, is an endothermic chemical reaction."
Explain.

> In photosynthesis, plants use energy from sunlight to convert carbon dioxide and water
> into sugar and oxygen. In an endothermic reaction, energy, in this case in the form of
> light energy, is absorbed. ∎

74) Item Type: Essay   Objective: 5-2.3
     Level: III   Tag: None

What does it mean to say that we understand many chemical reactions as transfers of
electrons? Explain.

> Because bonds are more likely to be formed when an atom has an incomplete outer energy
> level, many chemical reactions involve the sharing of electrons to complete an energy level.
> For example, when iron and oxygen combine to form rust, each iron atom loses electrons
> and each oxygen atom gains electrons. ∎

75) Item Type: Essay   Objective: 5-2.1
     Level: III   Tag: None

Explain why it is dangerous to burn a carbon-based fuel, such as propane or methane, in a
closed room or building.

> Methane or propane must burn in the presence of abundant oxygen if they are to produce
> carbon dioxide and water. If insufficient oxygen is present, carbon monoxide, a deadly
> gas, will be formed instead of carbon dioxide. ∎

76) Item Type: Essay   Objective: 5-3.1
     Level: III   Tag: None

Why is it incorrect to balance a chemical equation by changing the subscripts? Explain.

> The subscripts represent the number of atoms of each element in each chemical formula—if
> you change the subscripts, you change the compounds the formulas are describing. ∎

77) Item Type: Essay   Objective: 5-3.4
     Level: III   Tag: None

Why is the mole ratio an important concept for a scientist who frequently measures and
mixes chemicals in the lab? Explain.

> Because the mole ratio is derived from the balanced equation, if a scientist knows the
> equation that describes a reaction, and the atomic weights of the substances involved, he or
> she can determine the amount of each substance needed. ∎

78) Item Type: Essay   Objective: 5-4.1
      Level: III   Tag: None

Use chemical principles to describe why we store food in a refrigerator to keep it from spoiling. Give at least two examples.

> At lower temperatures, chemical reactions proceed more slowly. Therefore, milk will keep longer before curdling because the bacteria that cause curdling will grow more slowly and will not produce the acids that make spoiled milk taste bad. Also, mold will grow more slowly because the fungi will carry out the chemical process of digestion more slowly.

79) Item Type: Essay   Objective: 5-3.4
      Level: III   Tag: None

Explain how the Haber process for producing ammonia is a good example of Le Chatelier's principle.

> Le Chatelier's principle states that a rise in temperature favors the reactions that absorbs energy and makes less ammonia. If you have less nitrogen gas, and reduce the pressure, Le Chatelier's principle predicts that less ammonia will be produced. So to produce the most ammonia, you should have more heat and less pressure, as in the Haber process.

Chapter 6

1) Item Type: Multiple Choice   Objective: 6-1.1
Level: II   Tag: None

Which of the following is an example of a heterogeneous mixture?

           a) salt water   b) vinegar

           c) sugar solution   d) mayonnaise

d

2) Item Type: Multiple Choice   Objective: 6-1.1
Level: I   Tag: None

A heterogeneous mixture is one that is *not*

           a) uniform throughout.   b) easily mixed together.

           c) made of two or more   d) edible by humans.
           liquids.

a

3) Item Type: Multiple Choice   Objective: 6-1.1
Level: II   Tag: None

Which of the following is a homogeneous mixture?

           a) salad dressing   b) gelatin

           c) rubbing alcohol   d) orange juice with pulp

c

4) Item Type: Multiple Choice   Objective: 6-1.2
Level: I   Tag: None

A mixture that separates into different layers when you stop stirring it is

           a) a colloid.   b) a suspension.

           c) a solution.   d) an emulsion.

b

5) Item Type: Multiple Choice   Objective: 6-1.2
    Level: I   Tag: None

The particles in a colloid remain dispersed throughout the mixture because they

a) are extremely small.

b) have a positive charge.

c) have a negative charge.

d) are a combination of large and small particles.

a

6) Item Type: Multiple Choice   Objective: 6-1.2
    Level: I   Tag: None

Which statement about solutions is *incorrect*?

a) Liquids that mix to form a single layer are said to be miscible.

b) Solutions can be made of liquids and solids, liquids and liquids, or gases and liquids.

c) In a solution, the solvent is dissolved into the solute.

d) Solutions will not separate under normal circumstances.

c

7) Item Type: Multiple Choice   Objective: 6-1.3
    Level: I   Tag: None

You can usually filter out solid particles in a suspension by

a) pouring the less dense liquid off the top.

b) boiling it so that the solids are left behind.

c) distilling the entire suspension.

d) using a paper filter to catch the particles.

d

8) Item Type: Multiple Choice   Objective: 6-1.3
    Level: I   Tag: None

You can skim the fat off the top of a kettle of cold soup because fat is

a) made of small particles.

b) less dense than water and rises to the top.

c) an emulsion that remains dispersed throughout the soup.

d) made of large particles that will not pass through a filter.

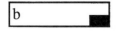
b

Chapter 6

9) Item Type: Multiple Choice   Objective: 6-1.3
    Level: I   Tag: None

Distillation can be used to separate solutions of miscible liquids because

        a) different liquids usually   b) boiling breaks the chemical
        have different boiling points.   bonds within each liquid.

        c) denser liquids sink to the   d) solids remain after the
        bottom.   liquids are boiled away.

a

10) Item Type: Multiple Choice   Objective: 6-2.1
    Level: I   Tag: None

Solubility refers to the

        a) size of the particles that   b) grams of solute per 100 g
        make up a substance.   of solvent.

        c) number of moles of solvent d) concentration of a solute
        dissolved per liter of solution. that is actually dissolved in a
                                   solvent.

b

11) Item Type: Multiple Choice   Objective: 6-2.1
    Level: I   Tag: None

Loose sugar dissolves much faster than a sugar cube because loose sugar has

        a) a greater surface area.   b) less kinetic energy.

        c) a higher temperature.   d) a greater surface tension.

a

12) Item Type: Multiple Choice   Objective: 6-2.1
    Level: I   Tag: None

Sugar will dissolve more quickly in iced tea if you stir it because stirring

        a) absorbs kinetic energy.   b) allows dissolved molecules
                              to diffuse through the tea.

        c) increases the solubility of   d) changes the electric charges
        the solution.   of the water molecules.

b

13) Item Type: Multiple Choice   Objective: 6-2.2
    Level: I   Tag: None

You can make a solute dissolve more quickly in a solvent by

        a) adding more solute.   b) adding ice.

        c) heating the solvent.   d) removing some solvent.

c

14) Item Type: Multiple Choice   Objective: 6-2.2
    Level: I   Tag: None

All of the following will make it easier to dissolve a solute in a solvent *except*

        a) heating the solvent.   b) stirring the solution.

        c) increasing the surface area   d) adding a larger amount of
        of the solute.   solute.

d

15) Item Type: Multiple Choice   Objective: 6-2.3
    Level: I   Tag: None

Water can dissolve charged particles because

        a) it is an ionic compound.   b) its atoms have partial charges.

        c) it is solid at a temperature   d) its molecular weight is
        of 0 degrees C.   extremely low.

b

16) Item Type: Multiple Choice   Objective: 6-2.3
    Level: I   Tag: None

Water is referred to as the universal solvent because

        a) it is found throughout the   b) all known substances
        universe.   dissolve in water.

        c) many different substances   d) it covers more than half of
        dissolve in water.   the Earth's surface.

c

17) Item Type: Multiple Choice   Objective: 6-2.4
    Level: I   Tag: None

An unsaturated solution is one that

a) can dissolve more solute at the current conditions.

b) will precipitate out all its dissolved solute.

c) can dissolve more solute only if heated.

d) can dissolve more solute only if the pressure is increased.

a

18) Item Type: Multiple Choice   Objective: 6-2.4
    Level: I   Tag: None

What happens when a supersaturated solution cools down?

a) The solution starts to freeze at room temperature.

b) The solution will accept even more solute.

c) The solute will rise to the top of the solution.

d) The solute will precipitate out of the solution.

d

19) Item Type: Multiple Choice   Objective: 6-3.1
    Level: I   Tag: None

Which statement about bases is *incorrect*?

a) All bases turn red litmus paper blue.

b) All bases contain hydroxide ions.

c) All bases taste bitter.

d) All bases feel slippery.

b

20) Item Type: Multiple Choice   Objective: 6-3.1
    Level: I   Tag: None

Acids are substances that

a) form hydronium ions when dissolved in water.

b) turn red litmus paper blue.

c) make foods taste bitter.

d) react with neutral liquids to form bases.

a

21) Item Type: Multiple Choice   Objective: 6-3.1
     Level: I   Tag: None

When dissolved in water, all acids will

         a) form hydroxide ions.   b) have a negative charge.

         c) conduct electricity.   d) turn blue.

c

22) Item Type: Multiple Choice   Objective: 6-3.3
     Level: I   Tag: None

A solution that is mildly acidic would have a pH of approximately

         a) 2.   b) 4.

         c) 6.   d) 8.

c

23) Item Type: Multiple Choice   Objective: 6-3.3
     Level: I   Tag: None

The pH of a substance is a measure of its

         a) boiling point.   b) food value.

         c) ability to mix with water.   d) hydronium ion concentration.

d

24) Item Type: Multiple Choice   Objective: 6-3.3
     Level: I   Tag: None

The label on a bottle indicates that the substance inside has a pH of 13. This tells you that the substance is

         a) neutral.   b) strongly acidic.

         c) mildly basic.   d) strongly basic.

d

Chapter 6

25) Item Type: Multiple Choice   Objective: 6-3.3
    Level: I   Tag: None

When a solution of an acid reacts with a solution of a base, hydronium ions react with hydroxide ions to form

        a) salt.   b) a stronger acid.

        c) a weaker base.   d) water.

> d

26) Item Type: Multiple Choice   Objective: 6-3.3
    Level: I   Tag: None

When a solution of an acid reacts with a solution of a base, the pH of the resulting solution depends on the

        a) amounts of acid and base   b) concentration of base alone.
        used.

        c) temperature of the acid and   d) concentration of acid alone.
        base used.

> a

27) Item Type: Multiple Choice   Objective: 6-3.3
    Level: I   Tag: None

What is a salt?

        a) A solution that contains a   b) An ionic compound that does
        strong acid   not contain oxide or hydroxide
                                         anions

        c) A substance formed by   d) A solution that contains more
        mixing two strong acids   anions than cations and is strongly
        together   acidic

> b

28) Item Type: Multiple Choice   Objective: 6-4.1
    Level: I   Tag: None

Which of the following is a basic solution?

        a) household ammonia   b) HCl dissolved in water

        c) vinegar   d) pure water

> a

29) Item Type: Multiple Choice   Objective: 6-4.1
    Level: I   Tag: None

Marinades for meat commonly include acids, such as vinegar or wine, because the acids can

a) toughen meat.   b) tenderize meat.

c) preserve meat.   d) react with salt to heighten flavor.

b

30) Item Type: Multiple Choice   Objective: 6-4.1
    Level: I   Tag: None

A disinfectant is a substance that

a) forms a base.   b) mixes safely with vinegar.

c) kills bacteria and viruses. d) forms an acid.

c

31) Item Type: Multiple Choice   Objective: 6-4.2
    Level: I   Tag: None

The products of soap-making are soap and

a) fat.   b) grease.

c) hard water.   d) glycerol.

d

32) Item Type: Multiple Choice   Objective: 6-4.2
    Level: I   Tag: None

Soap-making is a reaction between compounds found in animal fats and

a) glycerol or another alcohol.   b) negatively charged hydrocarbon chains.

c) sodium or potassium hydroxide solution.   d) sodium chloride.

c

33) Item Type: Multiple Choice   Objective: 6-4.2
    Level: I   Tag: None

Soap can remove grease and oil from your skin because it acts as

       a) an emulsifier to surround the oil.

       b) an acid to neutralize the dirt.

       c) a solvent to dissolve the dirt.

       d) a salt to make water harder.

a

34) Item Type: Multiple Choice   Objective: 6-4.3
    Level: I   Tag: None

Putting lemon juice on a piece of cut apple will

       a) make the fruit softer and easier to chew.

       b) prevent the fruit from turning brown.

       c) make the fruit taste sweeter.

       d) neutralize the acid in the fruit.

b

35) Item Type: Multiple Choice   Objective: 6-4.3
    Level: I   Tag: None

Yogurt is made by changing

       a) milk fat into an acid solution.

       b) acid in milk into a strong base.

       c) milk sugar into lactic acid.

       d) protein in milk into a denatured solid.

c

36) Item Type: Multiple Choice   Objective: 6-4.3
    Level: I   Tag: None

Which of the following chemicals is a base?

       a) lactose

       b) lemon juice

       c) aspirin

       d) baking soda

d

37) Item Type: Fill-in-the-Blank Objective: 6-1.1
    Level: I   Tag: None

Garden soil and potato salad are two examples of _____ mixtures.

heterogeneous

38) Item Type: Fill-in-the-Blank Objective: 6-1.1
    Level: I   Tag: None

A type of suspension that does not settle out under normal circumstances is a(n)

_____.

colloid

39) Item Type: Fill-in-the-Blank Objective: 6-1.1
    Level: I   Tag: None

A solution is an example of a(n) _____ mixture.

homogeneous

40) Item Type: Fill-in-the-Blank Objective: 6-1.2
    Level: I   Tag: None

The particles in a colloid are _____ than those in a suspension.

smaller

41) Item Type: Fill-in-the-Blank Objective: 6-1.2
    Level: I   Tag: None

A solution is more _____ than a suspension.

uniform

42) Item Type: Fill-in-the-Blank Objective: 6-1.2
    Level: I   Tag: None

Egg whites, paint, blood, and whipped cream are all examples of _____.

colloids

43) Item Type: Fill-in-the-Blank Objective: 6-1.3
    Level: I   Tag: None

You can separate two _____ by pouring the less dense liquid off the top.

immiscible liquids

Chapter 6

44) Item Type: Fill-in-the-Blank   Objective: 6-1.3
Level: I   Tag: None

When a solid is dissolved in water, you can separate the two by _____ or

_____.

evaporation; boiling or filtering

45) Item Type: Fill-in-the-Blank   Objective: 6-1.3
Level: I   Tag: None

The process used to separate two miscible liquids is _____.

distillation

46) Item Type: Fill-in-the-Blank   Objective: 6-2.1
Level: I   Tag: None

As sugar dissolves in water, sugar molecules _____, or spread through out the
entire solution.

diffuse

47) Item Type: Fill-in-the-Blank   Objective: 6-2.1
Level: I   Tag: None

A solute's _____ can often be increased by heating.

solubility

48) Item Type: Fill-in-the-Blank   Objective: 6-2.2
Level: I   Tag: None

Shaking or stirring a solution will make a solute _____ more quickly.

dissolve

49) Item Type: Fill-in-the-Blank   Objective: 6-2.2
Level: I   Tag: None

A solute will dissolve more quickly if you increase its _____ by breaking it into
small pieces.

surface area

50) Item Type: Fill-in-the-Blank   Objective: 6-2.2
Level: I   Tag: None

Solutes dissolve faster if the solvent is _____.

heated; hot

51) Item Type: Fill-in-the-Blank   Objective: 6-2.3
    Level: I   Tag: None

Water is a(n) _____ compound because its shared electrons are not spread evenly throughout each molecule.

polar

52) Item Type: Fill-in-the-Blank   Objective: 6-2.3
    Level: I   Tag: None

Because so many substances can dissolve in water, it is often referred to as the

_____.

universal solvent

53) Item Type: Fill-in-the-Blank   Objective: 6-2.3
    Level: I   Tag: None

A(n) _____ solution is an unstable system.

supersaturated

54) Item Type: Fill-in-the-Blank   Objective: 6-2.4
    Level: I   Tag: None

A saturated solution contains the greatest quantity of _____ that will dissolve in a given quantity of _____.

solute; solvent

55) Item Type: Fill-in-the-Blank   Objective: 6-3.1
    Level: I   Tag: None

A(n) _____ is a compound that can change color in a solution, depending on whether the solution is acidic or basic.

indicator

56) Item Type: Fill-in-the-Blank   Objective: 6-3.1
    Level: I   Tag: None

An acid is a substance that donates hydrogen ions (H^+) to form _____ ions when dissolved in water.

hydronium

Chapter 6

57) Item Type: Fill-in-the-Blank   Objective: 6-3.1
    Level: I   Tag: None

A(n) _____ is a substance that either contains hydroxide ions (OH^-) or reacts with water to form hydroxide ions.

base

58) Item Type: Fill-in-the-Blank   Objective: 6-3.2
    Level: I   Tag: None

Apple juice has a pH of 3, and stomach acid has a pH of 2. This means that stomach acid is _____ times more acidic than apple juice.

10

59) Item Type: Fill-in-the-Blank   Objective: 6-3.2
    Level: I   Tag: None

Baking soda has a pH of 9, and household ammonia has a pH of 12. This means that ammonia is _____ times more basic than baking soda.

1,000

60) Item Type: Fill-in-the-Blank   Objective: 6-3.2
    Level: I   Tag: None

pH is a measure of the _____ of a solution.

hydronium ion concentration

61) Item Type: Fill-in-the-Blank   Objective: 6-3.3
    Level: I   Tag: None

In a neutralization reaction, hydronium ions react with hydroxide ions to produce _____.

water

62) Item Type: Fill-in-the-Blank   Objective: 6-3.3
    Level: I   Tag: None

Salts are _____ formed when acids and bases react.

ionic compounds

63) Item Type: Fill-in-the-Blank   Objective: 6-3.3
    Level: I   Tag: None

Salts are ionic compounds that are often soluble in _____.

water

64) Item Type: Fill-in-the-Blank   Objective: 6-4.1
    Level: I   Tag: None

Because lye contains hydroxide ions, it is a _____ compound.

basic

65) Item Type: Fill-in-the-Blank   Objective: 6-4.1
    Level: I   Tag: None

Baking soda and baking powder are examples of _____ that are used in cooking.

bases

66) Item Type: Fill-in-the-Blank   Objective: 6-4.1
    Level: I   Tag: None

Another name for aspirin is _____.

acetylsalicylic acid

67) Item Type: Fill-in-the-Blank   Objective: 6-4.2
    Level: I   Tag: None

Soap works because the negatively charged end of the hydrocarbon chain dissolves in _____, whereas the neutral end dissolves in _____.

water; oil

68) Item Type: Fill-in-the-Blank   Objective: 6-4.2
    Level: I   Tag: None

Soap is made by reacting compounds made from _____ with a solution of sodium or potassium hydroxide.

animal fat

69) Item Type: Fill-in-the-Blank   Objective: 6-4.2
    Level: I   Tag: None

A byproduct of the chemical reaction that makes soap is _____.

glycerol

70) Item Type: Fill-in-the-Blank   Objective: 6-4.3
    Level: I   Tag: None

_____ make an upset stomach feel better because they _____ stomach acid.

Antacids; neutralize

71) Item Type: Fill-in-the-Blank   Objective: 6-4.3
     Level: I   Tag: None

Another name for vitamin C is _____.

ascorbic acid

72) Item Type: Fill-in-the-Blank   Objective: 6-4.3
     Level: I   Tag: None

Yogurt is made from milk when special bacteria turn _____, a sugar in milk, to

_____.

lactose; lactic acid

73) Item Type: Essay   Objective: 6-1.3
     Level: III   Tag: None

Explain why it would be difficult to separate two miscible liquids that have similar boiling points.

Miscible liquids are usually separated by distillation, a process that depends on the two liquids having different boiling points. If the boiling points of the liquids are similar, distillation cannot separate them.

74) Item Type: Essay   Objective: 6-1.1
     Level: III   Tag: None

Describe the difference between a suspension and an emulsion.

A suspension is a mixture of large-sized particles in a liquid. The particles quickly settle out when the mixture is allowed to stand. An emulsion is a mixture of two or more liquids evenly spread throughout one another. They do not separate.

75) Item Type: Essay   Objective: 6-2.2
     Level: III   Tag: None

Suppose you have a headache and you want the aspirin you take to work as quickly as possible. In what form should you take it?

Answers will vary but students should say that a crushed tablet or medication in liquid form will be absorbed faster than a whole tablet.

76) Item Type: Essay   Objective: 6-2.4
     Level: III   Tag: None

Explain what it means to say that a supersaturated solution is an unstable system.

Supersaturated solutions hold more dissolved solute than is specified by their solubility. They can only do so in special circumstances, such as if the solution is heated. They are unstable because as the solution cools, or as more solute is added, the excess solute will rapidly precipitate out.

77) Item Type: Essay   Objective: 6-3.1
   Level: III   Tag: None

Is it accurate to say that acids and bases are the opposite of one another? In what sense is this statement true?

> Acids are substances that contain hydrogen (H^+) ions. In water, acids form hydronium ions. Bases are substances that either contain hydroxide (OH^-) ions or react with water to form them. Acidic solutions contain more hydronium ions than hydroxide ions while the opposite is true of basic solutions.

78) Item Type: Essay   Objective: 6-3.1
   Level: III   Tag: None

List and describe one chemical reaction that depends on acid-base interactions.

> Answers will vary; students could include how a solution of sulfuric acid conducts electricity in car batteries.

79) Item Type: Essay   Objective: 6-4.2
   Level: III   Tag: None

Explain the difference between soap and detergent and why detergent cleans better under certain conditions.

> Both soaps and detergents are in the form of long hydrocarbon chains, but the charged end of a detergent is a sulfonate group ($-SO_3^-$) instead of a carboxylate group ($-COO^-$). As a result, detergents can lather in hard water (water that contains dissolved magnesium, calcium, or iron salts).

80) Item Type: Essay   Objective: 6-4.2
   Level: III   Tag: None

Describe some common household uses for acids and bases.

> Answers will vary but might include meat marinades (acids), bleach and ammonia (bases), baking soda (base), lactic acid used to make yogurt, ascorbic acid (Vitamin C).

Chapter 7

1) Item Type: Multiple Choice Objective: HRWPS 7-1.1
   Level: I Tag: None

Radioactive materials have unstable

    a) electrons.   b) nuclei.

    c) protons.   d) neutrons.

b

2) Item Type: Multiple Choice Objective: HRWPS 7-1.1
   Level: I Tag: None

After the nucleus of a radioactive element undergoes changes, the element can transform
into

    a) a different isotope of the   b) an entirely different
    same element.   element.

    c) both a and b   d) neither a nor b

c

3) Item Type: Multiple Choice Objective: HRWPS 7-1.1
   Level: I Tag: None

Alpha particles

    a) are positively charged.   b) consist of two protons and
                       four neutrons.

    c) can penetrate any thickness   d) all of the above
    of matter.

a

4) Item Type: Multiple Choice Objective: HRWPS 7-1.1
   Level: I Tag: None

Which of the following is not a type of nuclear radiation?

    a) alpha particles   b) beta particles

    c) neutrons emission   d) X-rays

d

Chapter 7

5)   Item Type: Multiple Choice   Objective: HRWPS 7-1.1
        Level: I   Tag: None

The type of nuclear radiation that can penetrate farthest through matter is called

        a) radons.   b) gamma rays.

        c) neutron emission.   d) X-rays.

    c

6)   Item Type: Multiple Choice   Objective: HRWPS 7-1.1
        Level: I   Tag: None

The process of nuclear change in an atom of radioactive material is called

        a) nuclear decay.   b) isotopes.

        c) nuclear mass.   d) radon.

    a

7)   Item Type: Multiple Choice   Objective: HRWPS 7-1.1
        Level: I   Tag: None

Nuclear radiation refers to charged particles or energy emitted by an unstable

        a) proton.   b) atom.

        c) nucleus.   d) isotope.

    c

8)   Item Type: Multiple Choice   Objective: HRWPS 7-1.2
        Level: I   Tag: None

In alpha decay, the mass number of the atom before the decay

        a) equals the sum of the mass   b) does not change after the
        numbers of the products.   decay.

        c) is the same as the atomic   d) cannot be determined.
        number.

    a

Chapter 7

9) Item Type: Multiple Choice   Objective: HRWPS 7-1.2
   Level: I   Tag: None

Alpha particles are nuclei of

a) oxygen.   b) nitrogen.

c) helium.   d) radium.

c ▪

10) Item Type: Multiple Choice   Objective: HRWPS 7-1.2
    Level: I   Tag: None

As beta particles ionize they

a) lose energy.   b) gain energy.

c) neither lose nor gain   d) none of the above.
energy.

b ▪

11) Item Type: Multiple Choice   Objective: HRWPS 7-1.2
    Level: I   Tag: Alpha decay

In this example of alpha decay, what is the mass number of radium before the decay?

a) 226   b) 88

c) 222   d) 226 + 88 (314)

a ▪

12) Item Type: Multiple Choice   Objective: HRWPS 7-1.2
    Level: I   Tag: Alpha decay

In this example, what are the chemical symbols of the products of the decay?

a) Ra and Rn   b) Ra and He

c) Rn and He   d) He is the only product.

c ▪

13) Item Type: Multiple Choice   Objective: HRWPS 7-1.2
    Level: I   Tag: None

During beta decay, a nucleus

    a) gives up two protons and   b) maintains the same number
    two neutrons.   of protons and neutrons.

    c) loses a proton and gains a   d) gains a proton and loses a
    neutron.   neutron.

d

14) Item Type: Multiple Choice   Objective: HRWPS 7-1.2
    Level: I   Tag: None

When a nucleus undergoes nuclear decay by gamma rays, the atomic number of the element

    a) remains the same.   b) increases by one.

    c) decreases by one.   d) increases by two.

a

15) Item Type: Multiple Choice   Objective: HRWPS 7-1.3
    Level: I   Tag: None

In radioactive decay, with each successive half-life, half the remaining sample decays to form another

    a) nucleus.   b) element.

    c) life-form.   d) proton.

b

16) Item Type: Multiple Choice   Objective: HRWPS 7-2.1
    Level: I   Tag: None

The attractive force between protons and neutrons in a nucleus caused by the strong nuclear force acts only

    a) outside the nucleus.   b) over a very short distance.

    c) only in unstable isotopes.   d) intermittently.

b

17) Item Type: Multiple Choice   Objective: HRWPS 7-2.1
    Level: I   Tag: None

Nuclei with too many or too few neutrons are

    a) never found.   b) unstable.

    c) unnatural.   d) stable.

b

18) Item Type: Multiple Choice   Objective: HRWPS 7-2.1
    Level: I   Tag: None

The process of the production of lighter nuclei from heavier nuclei is called

    a) mass energy.   b) fusion.

    c) magneticism.   d) fission.

d

19) Item Type: Multiple Choice   Objective: HRWPS 7-2.2
    Level: I   Tag: None

Fusion occurs when nuclei

    a) split.   b) combine.

    c) mutate.   d) gain energy.

b

20) Item Type: Multiple Choice   Objective: HRWPS 7-2.2
    Level: I   Tag: None

The opposite reaction to fusion is called

    a) beta decay.   b) alpha decay.

    c) fission.   d) neutron transmission.

c

21) Item Type: Multiple Choice   Objective: HRWPS 7-2.3
    Level: I   Tag: None

In the equation $E = mc^2$, "c" stands for

    a) carbon.   b) the total energy.

    c) the speed of light.   d) the size of the particle.

c

Chapter 7

22) Item Type: Multiple Choice   Objective: HRWPS 7-2.3
    Level: I   Tag: None

Which of the following events occurred first?

a) Einstein presents the special theory of relativity.

b) Hahn and Strassman discover nuclear fission.

c) Meitner and Frisch present their theory on the splitting of nuclei into smaller elements.

d) Fermi and his associates achieve the first controlled nuclear reaction.

a

23) Item Type: Multiple Choice   Objective: HRWPS 7-2.4
    Level: I   Tag: None

A fission chain reaction can be slowed by using materials that will

a) absorb some of the neutrons.

b) convert some of the neutrons to protons.

c) increase the rate of the neutron multiplication.

d) decrease the amount of available oxygen in the air.

a

24) Item Type: Multiple Choice   Objective: HRWPS 7-2.4
    Level: I   Tag: None

You prepare a large screened-in box, inside which you place several dozen mouse traps. You set each trap and on each mouse trap you place a ping pong ball. You then drop another ping pong ball into the box, which sets off one of the mouse traps, which sets off other mouse traps, and so on. You have just demonstrated

a) a chain reaction.

b) fusion.

c) the theory of relativity.

d) alpha decay.

a

25) Item Type: Multiple Choice   Objective: HRWPS 7-3.1
    Level: I   Tag: None

Background radiation can come from

a) the sun.

b) water.

c) plants.

d) all of the above

d

26) Item Type: Multiple Choice   Objective: HRWPS 7-3.1
     Level: I   Tag: None

Our body tissues are normally protected from most background radiation by

a) special deflectors in the   b) our outer skin.
atmosphere.

c) staying indoors or in   d) special molecules within
protected areas.   our bodies that fight radiation.

b

27) Item Type: Multiple Choice   Objective: HRWPS 7-3.1
     Level: I   Tag: None

Radon-222 is produced

a) by smoking cigarettes.   b) in nuclear power plants.

c) through a series of nuclear   d) as a result of rotting wood
reactions of uranium-238 in   in the basements of houses.
Earth's crust.

c

28) Item Type: Multiple Choice   Objective: HRWPS 7-3.1
     Level: I   Tag: None

After extensive radiation damage, a normal DNA molecule is likely to be rebuilt with an
incorrect sequencing of its

a) RNA.   b) electrons.

c) nitrogen bases.   d) alpha particles.

c

29) Item Type: Multiple Choice   Objective: HRWPS 7-3.2
     Level: I   Tag: None

Small radioactive sources that are present in smoke detectors release _____.

a) alpha particles   b) beta particles

c) gamma rays   d) neutrons

a

Chapter 7

30) Item Type: Multiple Choice Objective: HRWPS 7-3.2
    Level: I Tag: None

Short-lived isotopes like magnesium-28 that are used in fields such as geology, agriculture, and medicine are called

        a) trace elements.   b) radioactive tracers.

        c) carbon tracers.   d) alpha-emitting isotopes.

b

31) Item Type: Multiple Choice Objective: HRWPS 7-3.2
    Level: I Tag: None

The particles that are released by the radioactive sources in smoke alarms have charge and produce a(n)

        a) odor.   b) beam of light.

        c) electric current.   d) sound.

c

32) Item Type: Multiple Choice Objective: HRWPS 7-3.2
    Level: I Tag: None

Radioactive tracers are short-lived

        a) drugs.   b) isotopes.

        c) tumors.   d) rays.

b

33) Item Type: Multiple Choice Objective: HRWPS 7-3.2
    Level: I Tag: None

To treat certain brain tumors, doctors can use small beams of _____ that are focused to kill only the tumor cells.

        a) X-rays   b) beta rays

        c) alpha rays   d) gamma rays

d

34) Item Type: Multiple Choice   Objective: HRWPS 7-3.2
      Level: I   Tag: None

One beneficial use of radioactive iodine-131 is in the treatment of

        a) Graves's disease.   b) acne.

        c) radiation sickness.   d) leukemia.

a

35) Item Type: Multiple Choice   Objective: HRWPS 7-3.3
      Level: I   Tag: None

The use of nuclear reactors to generate electricity is

        a) decreasing rapidly.   b) found only in the United States.

        c) found in dozens of countries.   d) totally safe.

c

36) Item Type: Multiple Choice   Objective: HRWPS 7-3.3
      Level: I   Tag: None

According to current regulations, nuclear power plants in the US can be operated for

        a) 20 years.   b) 40 years.

        c) 50 years.   d) an indefinite length of time.

b

37) Item Type: Multiple Choice   Objective: HRWPS 7-3.3
      Level: I   Tag: None

The ideal location for a radioactive-waste storage facility is one that is

        a) in a sparsely populated area.   b) in an area free from earthquakes.

        c) far away from ground water   d) all of the above

d

Chapter 7

38) Item Type: Multiple Choice   Objective: HRWPS 7-3.3
    Level: I   Tag: None

When a fusion reactor for safely generating energy is developed, the element that could meet Earth's energy demands for millions of years is

        a) oxygen.   b) nitrogen.

        c) hydrogen.   d) lithium.

c

39) Item Type: Short Answer   Objective: HRWPS 7-1.1
    Level: I   Tag: None

What are massive, positively charged particles emitted by some radioactive elements?

alpha particles, helium nuclei

40) Item Type: Short Answer   Objective: HRWPS 7-1.1
    Level: I   Tag: None

What is the energy and matter released by radon gas that causes health concerns called?

nuclear radiation

41) Item Type: Short Answer   Objective: HRWPS 7-1.2
    Level: I   Tag: None

If the atomic number of an atom before alpha decay is 88, and one of its products has an atomic number of 86, what is the atomic number of the second product?

2

42) Item Type: Short Answer   Objective: HRWPS 7-1.2
    Level: I   Tag: None

Who was the scientist who showed that alpha particles are helium nuclei?

Ernest Rutherford

43) Item Type: Short Answer   Objective: HRWPS 7-1.2
    Level: I   Tag: Equation

In this example, the helium is also known as what?

the alpha particle

108

Chapter 7

44) Item Type: Short Answer   Objective: HRWPS 7-1.2
Level: 1   Tag: None

What type of particle is emitted when carbon-14 decays into nitrogen-14?

a beta particle

45) Item Type: Short Answer   Objective: HRWPS 7-1.3
Level: 1   Tag: None

What is the time required for half a sample of radioactive nuclei to decay called?

the half-life

46) Item Type: Short Answer   Objective: HRWPS 7-1.3
Level: 1   Tag: None

After three half-lives, what fraction of the original radioactive element remains?

one-eighth

47) Item Type: Short Answer   Objective: HRWPS 7-1.3
Level: 1   Tag: None

To determine the age of fairly recent remains (in the tens of thousands of years as opposed to millions of years), scientists compare the ratio of what two elements?

carbon-14 and carbon-12

48) Item Type: Short Answer   Objective: HRWPS 7-1.3
Level: 1   Tag: None

Potassium-40 decays into argon-40. Geologists use a technique to calculate the age of very old rocks by comparing the ratio of the amount of potassium-40 to argon-40. What is the technique?

radioactive decay rate / half-life

49) Item Type: Short Answer   Objective: HRWPS 7-2.1
Level: 1   Tag: None

A nucleus depends on the nuclear forces acting between the protons and the neutrons, which hold the nucleus together, to provide what?

stability

50) Item Type: Short Answer   Objective: HRWPS 7-2.1
Level: 1   Tag: None

What is the force that binds protons and neutrons together in a nucleus called?

strong nuclear force

51) Item Type: Fill-in-the-Blank   Objective: HRWPS 7-2.1
    Level: I   Tag: None

Nuclei with more than 83 protons are always unstable, no matter how many _____ they have.

neutrons

52) Item Type: Short Answer   Objective: HRWPS 7-2.1
    Level: I   Tag: None

The protons in a nucleus both repel and attract each other. In stable nuclei, which are stronger, the attractions or the repulsions?

the attractions

53) Item Type: Short Answer   Objective: HRWPS 7-2.1
    Level: I   Tag: Attractions and Repulsions

Name the interaction that binds protons and neutrons together in a nucleus.

a strong nuclear force

54) Item Type: Short Answer   Objective: HRWPS 7-2.2
    Level: I   Tag: None

The equivalence of mass and energy means that matter can be converted into energy and energy into matter. Write the equation that expresses this equivalence.

$E = mc^2$

55) Item Type: Short Answer   Objective: HRWPS 7-2.2
    Level: I   Tag: None

What is the process by which a nucleus splits into two or more smaller fragments, releasing neutrons and energy, called?

fission

56) Item Type: Short Answer   Objective: HRWPS 7-2.2
    Level: I   Tag: None

What is the name for the process in which light nuclei combine at extremely high temperatures, forming heavier nuclei and releasing energy?

fusion

57) Item Type: Short Answer   Objective: HRWPS 7-2.2
    Level: I   Tag: None

What is one example of a place where naturally occurring extreme temperatures provide the energy needed to bring hydrogen nuclei together in a fusion reaction?

stars

58) Item Type: Short Answer   Objective: HRWPS 7-2.3
Level: None   Tag: None

According to the theory of relativity, what does mass times the speed of light squared equal?

energy

59) Item Type: Short Answer   Objective: HRWPS 7-2.3
Level: 1   Tag: None

Who was the scientist who first presented the theory of relativity?

Albert Einstein

60) Item Type: Short Answer   Objective: HRWPS 7-2.3
Level: 1   Tag: None

In the equation, $E = mc^2$, what does the E stand for?

energy

61) Item Type: Short Answer   Objective: HRWPS 7-2.3
Level: 1   Tag: None

In the equation, $E = mc^2$, what does the m stand for?

mass

62) Item Type: Short Answer   Objective: HRWPS 7-2.3
Level: 1   Tag: None

In the equation, $E=mc^2$, what does c stand for?

the speed of light

63) Item Type: Short Answer   Objective: HRWPS 7-2.4
Level: 1   Tag: None

Name one good use of the energy produced in a controlled chain reaction.

generating electricity

64) Item Type: Fill-in-the-Blank   Objective: HRWPS 7-2.4
Level: 1   Tag: None

The ability to create a chain reaction depends on the number of _____ released.

neutrons

65) Item Type: Short Answer   Objective: HRWPS 7-3.1
Level: 1   Tag: None

What is nuclear radiation that is emitted from natural sources all around us called?

background radiation

66) Item Type: Short Answer   Objective: HRWPS 7-3.1
Level: 1   Tag: None

Ionization occurs when atoms lose or gain what?

electrons

67) Item Type: Short Answer   Objective: HRWPS 7-3.1
Level: 1   Tag: None

Leucopenia, hair loss, sterility, bone necrosis, and cancer are all common symptoms of what sickness?

radiation sickness

68) Item Type: Short Answer   Objective: HRWPS 7-3.1
Level: 1   Tag: None

Birth defects can occur when exposure to radiation causes damage to what part of reproductive cells?

DNA

69) Item Type: Short Answer   Objective: HRWPS 7-3.2
Level: 1   Tag: None

What is a short-lived isotope called that a geologist might use to follow underground water flow through an area?

a radioactive tracer

70) Item Type: Short Answer   Objective: HRWPS 7-3.3
Level: 1   Tag: None

Which is capable of producing the most energy, the known uranium reserves or the known reserves of coal and oil combined?

the known uranium reserves

71) Item Type: Short Answer   Objective: HRWPS 7-3.3
Level: 1   Tag: None

The main problem with disposing of radioactive wastes is that they have a long what?

half-life

Chapter 7

72) Item Type: Short Answer   Objective: HRWPS 7-3.3
    Level: I   Tag: None

What is the most likely fuel for nuclear-fusion reactors?

hydrogen

73) Item Type: Short Answer   Objective: HRWPS 7-3.3
    Level: I   Tag: None

In nuclear-fission reactors operating today, what is the most common fuel?

uranium-235

74) Item Type: Short Answer   Objective: HRWPS 7-1.1
    Level: I   Tag: None

What type of nuclear radiation can travel farthest through matter and why?

Gamma rays

75) Item Type: Essay   Objective: HRWPS 7-1.1
    Level: II   Tag: None

All four types of nuclear radiation have just been released simultaneously and are headed your way. Which will arrive first, which will have the greatest potential to cause damage to your tissues, and what can you do to protect yourself against each?

The fastest traveling type of nuclear radiation is gamma rays. They are also the hardest to protect against and have the most potential to cause damage because they penetrate farthest into matter. It takes a block of lead 7 cm thick to stop most gamma rays emitted during radioactive decay. Next would be the beta particles, which can be stopped by only 3 mm of aluminum or 10 mm of wood. The alpha particles are the slowest traveling of the types of nuclear radiation and are also the largest of the particles. Most of them can barely pass through a sheet of paper.

76) Item Type: Essay   Objective: HRWPS 7-1.2
    Level: I   Tag: None

A beta particle is negatively charged, but it comes from a positively charged nucleus. How is this possible?

Neutrons, which are not charged, decay to form a proton and an electron. The electron, which is negatively charged, is then ejected from the nucleus as a beta particle.

77) Item Type: Essay   Objective: HRWPS 7-1.3
    Level: II   Tag: None

Why do geologists use radioactive isotopes like potassium-40, rather than iodine-131, to calculate the age of rocks?

Iodine-131 has a half-life of only 8.1 days, so it would be practically nonexistent in a relatively short period of time. Potassium-40, on the other hand, has a half-life of 1,280,000,000 years, so it can be used to calculate the age of rocks that are billions of years old.

78) Item Type: Essay   Objective: HRWPS 7-1.3
    Level: III   Tag: None

You are working at an archaeological dig as the scientist in charge of determining the ages of things that are found. The archaeologists have just uncovered an area that appears to be an ancient dwelling.
A. What sorts of things do you need them to find to help you determine the age of the site?
B. There is approximately one-fourth the amount of carbon-14 in your samples as there is carbon-12. Is this significant and if so what does it tell you about the age of the samples?

A. You want the archaeologists to find any sorts of bones or other animal remains or preserved plant remains (such as might be found in an area where garbage was dumped). Also, any remnants of clothing will be helpful. If they can find a burial site, you can learn much.
B. All plants absorb carbon dioxide during photosynthesis, and a tiny fraction of the CO_2 molecules contain carbon-14 rather than the more common carbon-12. The amount of carbon-12 remains constant, whereas the carbon-14 decreases through beta decay. The half-life of carbon-14 is 5730 years, so if the ratio is approximately one-fourth that of living plants or animals, then the sample has undergone at least two half-lives and is over 11 500 years old.

79) Item Type: Essay   Objective: HRWPS 7-1.3
    Level: III   Tag: None

Describe a situation in which a scientist might want to use a short-lived isotope (tracers) like magnesium-28.

Scientists use radioactive tracers, which can be observed with sensitive detectors, to determine how fast ground water moves. In medicine, tracers are used to locate tumors or to follow the path of drugs through the body.

80) Item Type: Essay   Objective: HRWPS 7-1.3
    Level: I   Tag: None

Why can a small amount of mass (of matter) create a large amount of energy?

According to the theory of relativity, energy (E) is equal to mass (m) times the speed of light squared (c^2). The value of c is constant and is very large (3.0×10^8 m/s), and when it is squared it becomes 9.0×10^{16} J. This huge number times even a small mass will result in a large amount of energy.

81) Item Type: Essay   Objective: HRWPS 7-3.2
    Level: I   Tag: None

Describe how a tracer might be used in medicine to ensure that a drug is reaching the desired area.

Radioactive tracers can be used to trace the path of drugs that have been administered. Their progress and destination would be determined by equipment that is sensitive to radioactivity and can detect their presence.

82) Item Type: Essay   Objective: HRWPS 7-3.3
    Level: I   Tag: None

Name at least two disadvantages of a nuclear-fission reactor.

1. The products of fission reactions are often radioactive isotopes, which raise safety concerns.

2. Special shielding is required to prevent radiation from leaking into the surrounding environment.

3. Nuclear power plants can be operated for only about 40 years and then they must be shut down and dismantled. This makes them very expensive.

4. Nuclear waste has a very long half-life and must be stored for thousands if not millions of years.

1)   Tag Name: Alpha decay

$$^{226}_{88}\text{Ra} \longrightarrow ^{222}_{86}\text{Rn} + ^{4}_{2}\text{He} \quad \begin{matrix} 226 = 222 + 4 \\ 88 = 86 + 2 \end{matrix}$$

2)   Tag Name: Attractions and Repulsions

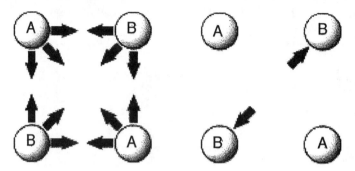

3)   Tag Name: Equation

$$^{226}_{88}\text{Ra} \rightarrow ^{222}_{86}\text{Rn} + ^{4}_{2}\text{He}$$

Copyright© by Holt, Rinehart and Winston. All rights reserved.

1) Item Type: Multiple Choice   Objective: 8-1.1
   Level: I   Tag: None

The distance traveled by an object divided by the time it takes to travel that distance is called

a) average velocity.   b) average speed.

c) average acceleration.   d) activity.

b

2) Item Type: Multiple Choice   Objective: 8-1.1
   Level: I   Tag: None

In order to determine speed, you must know

a) time.   b) distance.

c) both a and b   d) neither a nor b

c

3) Item Type: Multiple Choice   Objective: 8-1.1
   Level: I   Tag: None

What is the speed of an object at rest?

a) 15 km/h   b) 0 km/h

c) 1 km/h   d) This cannot be determined
                                   without further information.

b.

4) Item Type: Multiple Choice   Objective: 8-1.2
   Level: I   Tag: None

The difference between speed and velocity is that velocity includes

a) direction.   b) distance.

c) time.   d) weight.

a

Chapter 8

5)	Item Type: Multiple Choice	Objective: 8-1.2
	Level: II	Tag: None

An airplane is flying at 635 miles per hour at an altitude of 35 000 feet. It is currently over Kansas and is approximately 16 minutes ahead of its scheduled arrival time. What is its velocity?

a) 635 mi/h

b) 16 mi/min

c) 35 000 ft/s

d) This cannot be determined without further information about its direction.

d

6)	Item Type: Multiple Choice	Objective: 8-1.2
	Level: I	Tag: None

Which of the following does not indicate velocity?

a) 14 ft/s SSE

b) 40 mi/hr toward the town square along the main street

c) 80 km/hr going from New York toward New Jersey

d) 28 miles from Los Angeles to Catalina Island

d

7)	Item Type: Multiple Choice	Objective: 8-1.3
	Level: I	Tag: None

Which of the following is not a factor in calculating momentum?

a) mass

b) direction

c) acceleration

d) speed

c

8)	Item Type: Multiple Choice	Objective: 8-1.3
	Level: I	Tag: None

If you divide momentum by velocity, the result is the value of the object's

a) mass.

b) direction.

c) energy.

d) speed.

a

Chapter 8

9)   Item Type: Multiple Choice   Objective: 8-1.4
       Level: II   Tag: None

   Whenever an object is standing still, the value(s) that is/are always zero is/are

           a) speed.   b) velocity.

           c) momentum.   d) all of the above

   d

10)   Item Type: Multiple Choice   Objective: 8-1.4
       Level: I   Tag: None

   A 10.0 kg dog chasing a rabbit north at 6.0 m/s has a momentum of

           a) 0.6 kg·m/s.   b) 60.0 kg·m/s north.

           c) 60.0 m/s.   d) 60.0 kg/s.

   b

11)   Item Type: Multiple Choice   Objective: 8-1.4
       Level: III   Tag: None

   If you are given the mass of an object in pounds, the time in seconds, and the distance in
   feet, what must you do before you can calculate the momentum in SI units?

           a) convert the mass to   b) convert the distance to
              kilograms   meters

           c) convert the time to hours   d) all of the above

           e) only a and b above

   e

12)   Item Type: Multiple Choice   Objective: 8-2.1
       Level: I   Tag: None

   Acceleration is defined as the change in velocity divided by

           a) speed.   b) final velocity.

           c) time.   d) distance.

   c

13) Item Type: Multiple Choice   Objective: 8-2.1
     Level: I   Tag: None

The SI unit for acceleration is

     a) mph.   b) ft/sec^2.

     c) m/s^2.   d) $\Delta v \div t$.

c

14) Item Type: Multiple Choice   Objective: 8-2.1
     Level: I   Tag: None

On a velocity-time graph, a line with a negative slope indicates that the object is

     a) speeding up.   b) slowing down.

     c) accelerating.   d) traveling at a constant
                                  speed.

b

15) Item Type: Multiple Choice   Objective: 8-2.2
     Level: I   Tag: None

When the velocity of an object changes, it is acted upon by a(n)

     a) force.   b) inertia.

     c) momentum.   d) deceleration.

a

16) Item Type: Multiple Choice   Objective: 8-2.2
     Level: I   Tag: None

The combination of all of the forces acting on an object is called the

     a) total force.   b) union of forces.

     c) super force.   d) net force.

d

Chapter 8

17) Item Type: Multiple Choice   Objective: 8-2.2
     Level: I   Tag: None

If the net force acting on a stationary object is zero, then the object will

         a) accelerate in the direction of   b) remain at rest.
         the strongest force.

         c) begin moving backwards.   d) decelerate at a steady rate of
                                      speed.

b

18) Item Type: Multiple Choice   Objective: 8-2.3
     Level: I   Tag: None

If the net force on an object is zero then the object has

         a) reaction forces.   b) action forces.

         c) balanced forces.   d) unbalanced forces.

c

19) Item Type: Multiple Choice   Objective: 8-2.3
     Level: I   Tag: None

A tug-of-war that results in one team pulling the other across the line is an example of

         a) action forces.   b) reaction forces.

         c) balanced forces.   d) unbalanced forces.

d

20) Item Type: Multiple Choice   Objective: 8-2.3
     Level: I   Tag: None

Which of the following best illustrates balanced forces?

         a) a rock falling to the ground   b) a stretched rubber band being
                                      held between two hands

         c) a person lifting a heavy box   d) a crash between a large truck
         off of the ground   and a train

b

21) Item Type: Multiple Choice   Objective: 8-2.4
    Level: I   Tag: None

Friction is defined as

a) force that opposes motion between two surfaces that are touching.

b) rate at which velocity changes.

c) resistance of an object to a change in its velocity.

d) speed of an object in a particular direction.

a

22) Item Type: Multiple Choice   Objective: 8-2.4
    Level: II   Tag: None

A force is continuously applied to an object, causing it to accelerate. After a period of time, however, the object stops accelerating. What conclusions can be drawn?

a) The mass of the object has increased.

b) Gravity on the object has increased.

c) The object is experiencing some kind of friction.

d) The momentum of the object has reached a maximum.

c

23) Item Type: Multiple Choice   Objective: 8-2.4
    Level: I   Tag: None

Which of the following situations best demonstrates the effects of friction?

a) a parachutist descending to the ground

b) a loaded slingshot

c) an apple falling from a tree

d) two trucks colliding

a

24) Item Type: Multiple Choice   Objective: 8-2.4
     Level: I   Tag: None

Which of the following statements is true?

a) Frictional forces are greatest when both surfaces are rough.

b) When a truck is parked on a hill, friction is the force that is trying to pull the truck down the hill.

c) Air resistance is the opposite force from friction.

d) Friction can exist between two objects even when they are not in contact.

a

25) Item Type: Multiple Choice   Objective: 8-2.5
     Level: I   Tag: None

Weight is best described as

a) an object's resistance to acceleration.

b) what causes an object to fall.

c) the downward force exerted on objects due to gravity.

d) a force solely dependent on an object's mass.

c

26) Item Type: Multiple Choice   Objective: 8-2.5
     Level: I   Tag: None

When objects are moved further apart from each other, the force of gravity

a) increases.

b) stays the same.

c) decreases.

d) decreases at first and then increases.

c

27) Item Type: Multiple Choice   Objective: 8-2.5
     Level: I   Tag: None

Of the following, the greatest gravitational force would occur between

a) a marble and a baseball 5 meters apart.

b) a loaded freighter on the high seas and Earth.

c) the moon and an astronaut standing on the moon.

d) the moon and Earth.

d

28)   Item Type: Multiple Choice   Objective: 8-3.1
      Level: I   Tag: None

The law that states that every object maintains constant velocity unless acted on by an unbalanced force is

a) Newton's first law of motion.

b) Newton's second law of motion.

c) Newton's third law of motion.

d) the law of conservation of momentum.

a

29)   Item Type: Multiple Choice   Objective: 8-3.1
      Level: I   Tag: None

The law that states that for every action force there is an equal and opposite reaction force is

a) Newton's first law of motion.

b) Newton's second law of motion.

c) Newton's third law of motion.

d) the law of conservation of momentum.

c

30)   Item Type: Multiple Choice   Objective: 8-3.2
      Level: I   Tag: None

The law that states that the unbalanced force acting on an object equals the object's mass times its acceleration is

a) Newton's first law of motion.

b) Newton's second law of motion.

c) Newton's third law of motion.

d) the law of conservation of momentum.

b

31)   Item Type: Multiple Choice   Objective: 8-3.2
      Level: I   Tag: None

The SI unit of force, named for the scientist who described the relationship between motion and force, is called the

a) newton.

b) einstein.

c) curie.

d) pasteur.

a

124

32) Item Type: Multiple Choice   Objective: 8-3.2
    Level: I   Tag: None

One pound is equal to how many newtons?

a) 4.448 N   b) 2.2 N

c) 0.225 N   d) 12.5 N

a

33) Item Type: Multiple Choice   Objective: 8-3.3
    Level: I   Tag: None

Which of the following units is used to measure acceleration in free fall?

a) m/s   b) m•s

c) m/s^2 d) m^2/s^2

c

34) Item Type: Multiple Choice   Objective: 8-3.4
    Level: I   Tag: None

Which of the following equations is correct?

a) w = mg   b) w ≥ mg

c) w ≠ mg   d) w ≈ mg

a

35) Item Type: Multiple Choice   Objective: 8-3.4
    Level: I   Tag: None

Which of the following is true?

a) Weight and mass are   b) Weight is the gravitational force
proportional but not equal.   an object experiences due to its
                                  mass.

c) The weight of an object on Earth   d) all of the above
is greater than the weight of the
same object on the surface of the
moon, but the object's mass stays
the same.

d

36) Item Type: Multiple Choice   Objective: 8-3.5
    Level: I   Tag: None

When air resistance balances the weight of an object that is falling, the velocity

    a) slowly decreases.   b) remains constant.

    c) rapidly increases.   d) none of the above

b

37) Item Type: Multiple Choice   Objective: 8-3.5
    Level: I   Tag: None

What is the approximate terminal velocity of a sky diver before the parachute opens?

    a) 32 mi/h   b) 32 km/h

    c) 320 mi/h   d) 320 km/h

d

38) Item Type: Fill-in-the-Blank   Objective: 8-1.1
    Level: I   Tag: None

When an object covers equal distances in equal amounts of time, it is moving at a(n) _____ speed.

constant

39) Item Type: Short Answer   Objective: 8-1.1
    Level: I   Tag: None

Because the speed of an object can change from one instant to the next, dividing the distance covered by the time of travel gives _____.

the average speed

40) Item Type: Short Answer   Objective: 8-1.1
    Level: I   Tag: None

When an object is seen moving against a stationary background, what is the stationary background called?

the reference frame

41) Item Type: Fill-in-the-Blank   Objective: 8-1.2
    Level: I   Tag: None

Velocity describes both speed and _____.

| direction |

42) Item Type: Short Answer   Objective: 8-1.2
    Level: I   Tag: None

If an object traveling in one direction has a positive velocity, what kind of velocity would the same object traveling in the opposite direction have?

| negative velocity |

43) Item Type: Fill-in-the-Blank   Objective: 8-1.3
    Level: I   Tag: None

Mass times velocity equals _____.

| momentum |

44) Item Type: Short Answer   Objective: 8-1.3
    Level: I   Tag: None

Which has greater momentum, a small pick-up truck traveling at 55 mi/hr or a full-sized bus traveling at the same speed?

| the bus |

45) Item Type: Short Answer   Objective: 8-1.3
    Level: I   Tag: None

A large truck loaded with scrap steel weighs 14 tons and is traveling north on the interstate heading for Chicago. It has been averaging 48 mi/hr for the journey and has traveled over 1450 miles so far. It has just stopped to refuel. What is its current momentum?

| 0 (zero) |

46) Item Type: Short Answer   Objective: 8-1.3
    Level: I   Tag: None

If two objects with different masses and traveling with different velocities collide, what law allows you to predict the motion of the objects after the collision?

| the law of conservation of momentum |

47) Item Type: Short Answer   Objective: 8-1.4
Level: II   Tag: None

A small sports car traveling south collides with a heavy truck traveling north. Both vehicles are going at the same speed. Which will be moved off course by the collision and in which direction?

> sports car will be moved north

48) Item Type: Short Answer   Objective: 8-1.4
Level: III   Tag: None

If two vehicles collide, name at least one outside force that will come into effect immediately after the impact and cause the objects to eventually come to a stop.

> gravity / friction / wind resistance

49) Item Type: Short Answer   Objective: 8-2.1
Level: I   Tag: None

Define acceleration.

> Acceleration is the rate at which velocity changes.

50) Item Type: Short Answer   Objective: 8-2.1
Level: II   Tag: None

In your own words, explain the similarities and differences between velocity and acceleration.

> Both involve a change over time. However, velocity is the rate of change of the object's position, whereas acceleration is the rate of change of the object's velocity.

51) Item Type: Short Answer   Objective: 8-2.1
Level: I   Tag: None

Explain why a cyclist accelerates when turning a corner even if her speed doesn't change.

> Acceleration is any change in velocity, and velocity involves both speed and direction. Therefore, the cyclist accelerates when turning because there is a change in her direction even if there is no change in her speed.

52) Item Type: Short Answer   Objective: 8-2.1
Level: II   Tag: None

During a race, a sprinter increases from 5.0 m/s to 7.5 m/s over a period of 1.25 s. What is the sprinter's average acceleration during this period?

> 2.0 m/s^2

53) Item Type: Short Answer   Objective: 8-2.2
    Level: II   Tag: None

Two archers shoot identical arrows at a target from exactly opposite directions. Use your knowledge of net forces to describe the movement of the target.

> Because the forces are equal, the net force will be zero and the target will not move.

54) Item Type: Short Answer   Objective: 8-2.3
    Level: I   Tag: None

Distinguish between balanced forces and unbalanced forces.

> Balanced forces combine to produce a net force that is equal to zero, whereas unbalanced forces combine to produce a net nonzero force.

55) Item Type: Short Answer   Objective: 8-2.3
    Level: I   Tag: None

What will the result be if two equal forces act on a single object from different directions that are not exactly opposite?

> The resulting net force will cause the object to accelerate—it will change its speed, direction, or both.

56) Item Type: Short Answer   Objective: 8-2.4
    Level: II   Tag: None

Why is it easier to push a crate over a smooth concrete sidewalk than over grass?

> On the grass, the crate experiences more friction.

57) Item Type: Short Answer   Objective: 8-2.4
    Level: III   Tag: None

You are pushing a heavy crate across a cement floor when you hit a section of flooring covered with smooth steel plates. Suddenly it is somewhat easier to push the crate. Why?

> The smooth steel plates provide less friction against the crate than the rough cement floor. The crate moves more easily.

58) Item Type: Short Answer   Objective: 8-2.4
    Level: II   Tag: None

List two situations in which friction is helpful or necessary.

> When trying to walk or drive on icy sidewalks or streets; between sandpaper and the wood that you are trying to make smooth; when trying to slow down a vehicle; when parking a vehicle on a sloped surface; when trying to warm your hands by rubbing them together. [Accept all reasonable answers.]

59) Item Type: Short Answer   Objective: 8-3.1
    Level: II   Tag: None

State Newton's first law.

> An object at rest remains at rest and an object in motion maintains its velocity unless it experiences an unbalanced force.

60) Item Type: Short Answer   Objective: 8-3.1
    Level: II   Tag: None

State Newton's second law.

> The unbalanced force acting on an object equals the object's mass times its acceleration.

61) Item Type: Fill-in-the-Blank   Objective: 8-3.2
    Level: I   Tag: None

According to Newton's second law of motion, force is the product of _____ and _____.

> mass; acceleration

62) Item Type: Short Answer   Objective: 8-3.2
    Level: I   Tag: None

Express the following as an equation: One newton is the force that can give an object with a mass of 1 kg an acceleration of 1 m/s^2.

> $1 \text{ N} = 1 \text{ kg} \times 1 \text{ m/s}^2$

63) Item Type: Short Answer   Objective: 8-3.2
    Level: II   Tag: None

Rearrange the equation for Newton's second law of motion to define acceleration in terms of force and mass.

> $a = F \div m$

64) Item Type: Short Answer   Objective: 8-3.3
    Level: I   Tag: None

What is free fall?

> Free fall is the motion of an object resulting from only the force of gravity.

65) Item Type: Short Answer   Objective: 8-3.3
    Level: I   Tag: None

Where is the free fall acceleration of an object under Earth's gravity directed?

> toward the center of Earth

Chapter 8

66) Item Type: Short Answer   Objective: 8-3.3
    Level: 1   Tag: None

What is the value for the acceleration of objects in free fall near Earth?

9.81 m/s^2

67) Item Type: Short Answer   Objective: 8-3.3
    Level: 1   Tag: None

In the absence of air resistance, how would the acceleration of a 1.5 kg book and the acceleration of a 15 kg rock differ if the objects were dropped from the same height?

They would not differ; they would be the same.

68) Item Type: Short Answer   Objective: 8-3.3
    Level: 1   Tag: None

Does the direction of an object falling toward Earth differ from the direction of an object falling through water on Earth? Why or why not?

The gravitational force of Earth is always directed toward the center of Earth, so the two objects would both fall toward the center of Earth.

69) Item Type: Short Answer   Objective: 8-3.4
    Level: 1   Tag: None

What is the difference between mass and weight?

Mass is a measure of the amount of matter in an object. Weight is the gravitational force an object experiences due to its weight.

70) Item Type: Short Answer   Objective: 8-3.4
    Level: 1   Tag: None

How does gravity influence the shapes of living things?

On land, large animals must have strong skeletons to support their mass against gravity. Large plants such as trees need sturdier trunks for the same reason.

71) Item Type: Short Answer   Objective: 8-3.5
    Level: II   Tag: None

Define terminal velocity.

Terminal velocity is the maximum velocity reached by a falling object, occurring when resistance of the medium is equal to the force due to gravity.

72) Item Type: Short Answer   Objective: 8-3.5
     Level: II   Tag: None

How would the terminal velocity of an object falling toward Earth differ from the terminal velocity of the same object falling through water and why?

The object's terminal velocity through water would be less because the resistance created by water is greater than the resistance created by air.

73) Item Type: Short Answer   Objective: 8-3.5
     Level: I   Tag: None

Why does it require less fuel to accelerate a rocket in outer space than required in Earth's atmosphere?

The main factor is that the gravity is stronger close to Earth. Also, the air in Earth's atmosphere is more dense, so the air resistance is greater and it takes more fuel to accelerate.

74) Item Type: Short Answer   Objective: 8-3.5
     Level: I   Tag: None

What is the velocity of an object called when gravitational forces and air resistance equalize on an object that is falling toward Earth and the object stops accelerating?

terminal velocity

75) Item Type: Essay   Objective: 8-1.1
     Level: III   Tag: None

You have two photos of a person walking. One shows the person at the corner of Third and Main streets, the other shows the person at the corner of Tenth and Main streets. There are lampposts at every corner in this town, and the first picture shows it to be 10:32:00 exactly. The second picture shows it to be 10:49:30. You know three facts: (1) All of the clocks are synchronized; (2) there are exactly 12 equal-sized blocks per mile in this town; and (3) the streets that cross Main in this area are numbered consecutively, with no interruptions.

What is the person's average speed in miles per hour (rounded off to the nearest tenth)?

If there are 12 blocks per mile, the person walks seven-twelfths of a mile [approx. 0.58 mi] in 17.5 minutes [0.29 hr]. In mi/hr this would be 0.58 ÷ 0.29 = 2.0 mi/hr.

76) Item Type: Essay   Objective: 8-2.5
      Level: III   Tag: None

A tube of air contains a feather and a coin. Both objects are dropped at the same time. The coin falls faster than the feather. However, when the air is removed from the tube to create a vacuum, both the feather and the coin reach the bottom at the same time. Explain why this happens.

> In the first case, the air provides more resistance (friction) to the motion of the feather than to that of the coin, so the coin falls faster. In a vacuum there is no air to provide resistance to the objects, so only the force of gravity is acting upon them and they fall at the same rate.

77) Item Type: Essay   Objective: 8-3.1
      Level: III   Tag: None

Using the terms acceleration, velocity, speed, and inertia, explain why wearing seat belts saves lives. Also explain why shoulder belts and lap belts used together are more effective than lap belts alone.

> Whenever the velocity of a car changes, whether by speeding up, slowing down, or changing directions, its acceleration also changes. If a moving car comes to a quick stop, it experiences a form of acceleration. Your body feels this acceleration as a push forward because of inertia, or your body's resistance to a change in velocity. Shoulder belts and lap belts hold you in place, counteracting this inertia, and prevent you from being seriously injured or killed by hitting the dashboard or by flying through the windshield. Used together, they prevent both your upper and lower body from continuing to move forward. Lap belts alone would keep your lower body in place, but your upper body could still be driven forward against the steering wheel or dashboard.

78) Item Type: Essay   Objective: 8-3.1
      Level: I   Tag: None

Using Newton's first law of motion in your answer, explain why a baby is better off riding in a car when it is placed in a special car seat that faces backward rather than forward.

> In cases of sudden stops in an automobile, inertia will force any passengers forward. If a baby is in a car seat that is facing forward, the only area resisting the inertia will be at the baby's waist area where the seat belt restrains the baby. The tremendous force could cause serious internal injury to the baby. Also, whipping forward and then suddenly backward could cause a whiplash injury to the baby's neck. If the baby is secured in a backward-facing car seat, the force that is needed to bring the baby to a stop would be spread out over its entire body.

79) Item Type: Essay   Objective: 8-3.1
     Level: II   Tag: None

Explain how a skyrocket works using one of Newton's laws of motion.

> The fuse is ignited, which in turn ignites the gunpowder inside the skyrocket, and the air around the gunpowder begins to expand rapidly. If the tube containing the gunpowder were tightly sealed on all sides and ends it would explode. However, one end of the rocket is not tightly sealed, allowing the hot gases to escape. These escaping gases create a force, and according to Newton's third law of motion, for every action force there is an equal and opposite reaction force, so the skyrocket reacts by accelerating forward.

80) Item Type: Essay   Objective: 8-3.4
     Level: I   Tag: None

Explain why organisms that live in water don't need as strong a skeletal structure as organisms that live on land.

> There is nothing on land to counteract the force of gravity, so organisms must develop strong structures to support their mass against it. In water, the downward force of gravity is balanced by the upward forces of the water, so strong skeletons and other supporting structures are unnecessary.

81) Item Type: Essay   Objective: 8-3.5
     Level: III   Tag: None

When a skydiver jumps from an airplane, his terminal velocity before opening the parachute reaches approximately 320 km/h. Why does the rate of descent of the skydiver slow when the parachute opens? After all, the skydiver still has the same mass.

> When the skydiver's parachute is unopened, his surface area is much less than when the parachute is open. Therefore, the air resistance is much less and the skydiver will fall at a faster rate. Once the parachute opens, the surface area of the parachute creates far more resistance with the air and the skydiver's descent is slowed. The force of gravity is exactly the same and the mass has not changed, but the air resistance is greater.

Chapter 9

1)   Item Type: Multiple Choice   Objective: 9-1.1
            Level: I   Tag: None

A boy pushes on a parked car with a force of 200 N. The car does not move. How much work does the boy do on the car?

       a) 200 N   b) 200 J

       c) zero   d) can't be determined

c

2)   Item Type: Multiple Choice   Objective: 9-1.1
            Level: I   Tag: None

What are the units of work?

       a) J   b) N·m

       c) $kg \cdot m^2/s^2$ d) all of the above

d

3)   Item Type: Multiple Choice   Objective: 9-1.1
            Level: III   Tag: None

Which of the following processes requires the most work?

       a) A 10 kg weight rests on a table.   b) A person holds a 1 kg weight still with outstretched arms.

       c) A person lifts a 1 kg weight 1 m off the floor.   d) A 10 kg ball is rolled across the floor at a constant speed for a distance of 10 m.

c

4)   Item Type: Multiple Choice   Objective: 9-1.1
            Level: II   Tag: None

A man pushes a crate along a factory floor by exerting a force of 55 N. If the crate moves a distance of 4.0 m, how much work does the man perform?

       a) 165 N   b) 220 N

       c) zero   d) 145 J

b

5)   Item Type: Multiple Choice   Objective: 9-1.1
       Level: II   Tag: None

What are the units of power?

           a) watts   b) horsepower

           c) joules per second   d) all of the above

d

6)   Item Type: Multiple Choice   Objective: 9-1.2
       Level: I   Tag: None

A weightlifter presses a 400 N weight 0.5 m over his head in 2 seconds. What is the power of the weightlifter?

           a) 100 N   b) 25 watts
           c) 400 watts   d) 100 watts

d

7)   Item Type: Multiple Choice   Objective: 9-1.4
       Level: II   Tag: None

What is the mechanical advantage of a ramp that is 10 meters long and 2 meters high?

           a) 20   b) 5

           c) 8   d) 15

b

8)   Item Type: Multiple Choice   Objective: 9-1.3
       Level: II   Tag: None

A machine is a device that

           a) requires less work to do a   b) decreases the amount of
           given task.   work done by a given force.

           c) increases energy.   d) can multiply and change the
                                             direction of an input force.

d

9) Item Type: Multiple Choice   Objective: 9-2.1
   Level: II   Tag: None

A first-class lever has the

a) fulcrum at one end and the output force between the fulcrum and the input force.

b) fulcrum at one end and the input force between the fulcrum and the output force

c) fulcrum in the middle.

d) input force in the middle.

c

10) Item Type: Multiple Choice   Objective: 9-2.1
    Level: II   Tag: None

A wheelbarrow is an example of a

a) first-class lever.

b) second-class lever.

c) third-class lever.

d) fourth-class lever.

b

11) Item Type: Multiple Choice   Objective: 9-2.1
    Level: II   Tag: None

Which of the following is an example of a third-class lever?

a) a nutcracker

b) a hand-held boat paddle

c) a crow bar

d) a screw

b

12) Item Type: Multiple Choice   Objective: 9-2.3
    Level: II   Tag: None

Which of the following is not a simple machine?

a) a lever

b) a pair of scissors

c) a screw

d) a wheel and axle

b

Chapter 9

13) Item Type: Multiple Choice   Objective: 9-2.2
     Level: I   Tag: None

What is the mechanical advantage of a single fixed pulley?

a) 1   b) 1.5

c) 2   d) 3

a

14) Item Type: Multiple Choice   Objective: 9-2.2
     Level: II   Tag: None

What is the mechanical advantage of a single movable pulley?

a) 1   b) 1.5
c) 2   d) 3

c

15) Item Type: Multiple Choice   Objective: 9-2.3
     Level: I   Tag: None

Which of the following is an example of a wheel and axle?

a) a block and tackle   b) a pulley

c) a screwdriver   d) a nutcracker

c

16) Item Type: Multiple Choice   Objective: 9-2.2
     Level: II   Tag: None

An inclined plane

a) changes the direction of the   b) changes the magnitude of
force only.   the force only.

c) changes both the magnitude   d) decreases the amount of
and the direction of the force.   work done.

c

17) Item Type: Multiple Choice   Objective: 9-2.1
    Level: I   Tag: None

Which of the following is not in the inclined plane family?

    a) a wedge   b) a screw

    c) a ramp   d) a wheel and axle

d

18) Item Type: Multiple Choice   Objective: 9-2.3
    Level: II   Tag: None

Which of the following is a compound machine?

    a) a wheel and axle   b) a pulley

    c) a pair of pliers   d) a ramp

c

19) Item Type: Multiple Choice   Objective: 9-3.1
    Level: III   Tag: None

Which of the following statements about work and energy is not true?

    a) When work is done, energy   b) Energy may be defined as
    is transferred or transformed.   the ability to do work.

    c) Work and energy are   d) Work and energy have the
    always equal.   same units.

c

20) Item Type: Multiple Choice   Objective: 9-3.3
    Level: II   Tag: None

What is the gravitational potential energy of a 55 kg box that is 8.0 m above the ground?

    a) 5500 J   b) 3400 J

    c) 4300 J   d) 550 J

c

21) Item Type: Multiple Choice   Objective: 9-3.2
    Level: I   Tag: None

Gravitational potential energy depends on the

        a) the mass of the object.   b) the height of the object.

        c) the acceleration due to   d) All of the above
        gravity.

d

22) Item Type: Multiple Choice   Objective: 9-3.3
    Level: II   Tag: None

A medicine ball has a mass of 5 kg and is thrown with a speed of 2 m/s. What is its kinetic energy?

        a) 100 J   b) 10 J
        c) 2000 J   d) 500 J

b

23) Item Type: Multiple Choice   Objective: 9-3.4
    Level: II   Tag: None

Which of the following is an example of mechanical energy?

        a) nuclear energy   b) chemical energy

        c) potential energy   d) light energy

c

24) Item Type: Multiple Choice   Objective: 9-3.5
    Level: II   Tag: None

The kind of energy associated with atomic bonds is

        a) nuclear energy.   b) light energy.

        c) chemical energy.   d) kinetic energy.

c

25) Item Type: Multiple Choice   Objective: 9-3.5
    Level: II   Tag: None

The primary source of the sun's energy is

        a) chemical energy.   b) nuclear fusion.

        c) nuclear fission.   d) potential energy.

b

26) Item Type: Multiple Choice   Objective: 9-4.1
    Level: III   Tag: None

A pendulum is swinging back and forth and has a kinetic energy of 400 J at a particular
point in its path. Which of the following statements is not true?

        a) Both the kinetic and   b) The minimum kinetic
        potential energy are   energy is zero.
        decreasing.

        c) When the kinetic energy is   d) The potential energy
        zero, the potential energy will   increases when the kinetic
        be 400 J greater.   energy decreases.

a

27) Item Type: Multiple Choice   Objective: 9-4.1
    Level: II   Tag: None

Which of the following statements is not true?

        a) The energy of a closed   b) The energy of an open
        system is constant.   system can increase.

        c) If the kinetic energy of an   d) Energy cannot be created or
        object decreases, the   destroyed.
        nonmechanical energy will
        decrease.

c

Chapter 9

28) Item Type: Multiple Choice Objective: 9-4.3
Level: II Tag: None

The efficiency of a ramp is 75%. If the amount of work input is 240 J, what is the amount of useful work output?

a) 320 J

b) 310 J

c) 240 J

d) 180 J

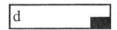

29) Item Type: Multiple Choice Objective: 9-1.2
Level: II Tag: None

The brakes on a car exert a frictional force of 6000 N in getting the car to stop. If the work done by the brakes is 120 000 J in coming to a stop, how many meters did the car travel after the driver applied the brakes?

a) 6 m

b) 20 m

c) 12 m

d) 40 m

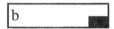

30) Item Type: Multiple Choice Objective: 9-2.3
Level: III Tag: Picture of a hand using a pair of tweezers

A pair of tweezers is

a) a first-class lever.

b) a compound machine made of two third-class levers.

c) a compound machine made of two second-class levers.

d) a kind of wedge.

31) Item Type: Multiple Choice Objective: 9-1.2
Level: II Tag: None

An object weighing 75 N is dropped from the top of a building and falls a distance of 28 m to the ground. How much work does gravity do on the object from the time it is dropped to the time it hits the ground?

a) zero

b) 75 J

c) 2100 J

d) 4625 J

Chapter 9

32) Item Type: Multiple Choice   Objective: 9-3.3
     Level: II   Tag: None

An object has a kinetic energy of 810 J after falling a certain distance. If the mass of the object is 20 kg, what is the speed of the object at this time?

    a) cannot be determined   b) 9 m/s

    c) 8 m/s   d) 7 m/s

b

33) Item Type: Multiple Choice   Objective: 9-4.2
     Level: I   Tag: None

The law of conservation of energy states that

    a) the energy of a system can   b) it is impossible to make a
    disappear.   perpetual motion machine.

    c) energy cannot change form.   d) energy can neither be
                                     created nor destroyed.

d

34) Item Type: True-False   Objective: 9-1.3
     Level: II   Tag: None

If a person tries to lift a heavy box for 5 seconds and can't make it budge, the work done on the box is equal to the amount of energy the person uses.

F

35) Item Type: Fill-in-the-Blank   Objective: 9-1.1
     Level: I   Tag: None

_____ is a quantity that measures the effects of a force acting over a distance.

Work

36) Item Type: Fill-in-the-Blank   Objective: 9-1.1
     Level: I   Tag: None

_____ is a quantity that measures the rate at which work is done.

Power

37) Item Type: Fill-in-the-Blank   Objective: 9-1.3
    Level: I   Tag: None

_____ is a quantity that measures how much a machine multiplies force or distance.

| Mechanical advantage ■ |

38) Item Type: True-False   Objective: 9-1.3
    Level: I   Tag: None

Machines decrease the amount of energy that is needed to do work.

| F ■ |

39) Item Type: Fill-in-the-Blank   Objective: 9-1.1
    Level: I   Tag: None

Power is calculated by dividing work by _____ .

| time ■ |

40) Item Type: Fill-in-the-Blank   Objective: 9-1.1
    Level: I   Tag: None

Horsepower is the common unit of power in rating engines. However, the official SI unit of power is the _____ .

| watt ■ |

41) Item Type: True-False   Objective: 9-1.1
    Level: I   Tag: None

Because of friction, using machines increases the amount of energy that is needed to do work.

| T ■ |

42) Item Type: Fill-in-the-Blank   Objective: 9-2.1
    Level: I   Tag: None

All levers have a rigid arm that turns around a point called the _____ .

| fulcrum ■ |

43) Item Type: True-False   Objective: 9-2.1
    Level: I   Tag: None

A pulley system always causes the direction of the output force to be opposite to the direction of the input force.

| F ■ |

44) Item Type: Fill-in-the-Blank   Objective: 9-2.3
     Level: I   Tag: None

A _____ is defined as a machine made up of more than one simple machine.

compound machine

45) Item Type: True-False   Objective: 9-2.2
     Level: II   Tag: None

A first-class lever can have an input force greater than the output force.

T

46) Item Type: True-False   Objective: 9-2.2
     Level: II   Tag: None

A second-class lever always has an input force that is less than the output force.

T

47) Item Type: Fill-in-the-Blank   Objective: 9-2.1
     Level: I   Tag: None

A(n) _____ is an inclined plane wrapped around a cylinder.

screw

48) Item Type: True-False   Objective: 9-2.2
     Level: II   Tag: None

Increasing the angle a ramp makes with the horizontal decreases the mechanical advantage.

T

49) Item Type: Fill-in-the-Blank   Objective: 9-3.1
     Level: I   Tag: None

_____ can be defined as the ability to do work.

Energy

50) Item Type: Fill-in-the-Blank   Objective: 9-3.2
     Level: I   Tag: None

The formula for calculating kinetic energy can be written as _____ .

$KE = 1/2 \ mv^2$

Chapter 9

51) Item Type: Fill-in-the-Blank   Objective: 9-3.2
    Level: I   Tag: None

    _____ is the stored energy resulting from the relative positions of objects in a
    system.

    | Potential energy ▄ |

52) Item Type: Fill-in-the-Blank   Objective: 9-3.2
    Level: I   Tag: None

    _____is the energy of a moving object due to its motion.

    | Kinetic energy ▄ |

53) Item Type: Fill-in-the-Blank   Objective: 9-3.4
    Level: I   Tag: None

    The sum of the kinetic and potential energy of large-scale objects in a system is called

    _____.

    | mechanical energy ▄ |

54) Item Type: Fill-in-the-Blank   Objective: 9-3.4
    Level: I   Tag: None

    Energy that lies at the level of atoms and does not affect motion on a large scale is
    sometimes called _____ energy.

    | nonmechanical ▄ |

55) Item Type: Fill-in-the-Blank   Objective: 9-3.5
    Level: I   Tag: None

    The source of the energy when dynamite explodes is _____ energy.

    | chemical ▄ |

56) Item Type: Fill-in-the-Blank   Objective: 9-3.5
    Level: I   Tag: None

    The process that transforms light energy into chemical energy in plants is called

    _____.

    | photosynthesis ▄ |

57) Item Type: Fill-in-the-Blank   Objective: 9-3.5
    Level: I   Tag: None

    The source of the sun's energy is _____.

    | nuclear fusion ▄ |

Chapter 9

58) Item Type: True-False   Objective: 9-3.5
    Level: II   Tag: None

The flow of charged particles through a conductor is a form of energy called electricity.

> T

59) Item Type: Fill-in-the-Blank   Objective: 9-4.2
    Level: II   Tag: None

When a system exchanges energy with the environment outside the system, it is called a(n) _____.

> open system

60) Item Type: Fill-in-the-Blank   Objective: 9-4.2
    Level: I   Tag: None

A(n) _____ exchanges energy with the outside.

> open system

61) Item Type: True-False   Objective: 9-4.2
    Level: III   Tag: None

A meteorologist trying to predict global warming would consider Earth to be a closed system.

> F

62) Item Type: True-False   Objective: 9-4.2
    Level: III   Tag: None

A ball falling under the force of gravity is a closed system.

> F

63) Item Type: Fill-in-the-Blank   Objective: 9-4.3
    Level: I   Tag: None

_____ measures the ratio of useful work output to work input.

> Efficiency

64) Item Type: True-False   Objective: 9-4.3
    Level: II   Tag: None

Increasing the length of a ramp increases the efficiency of the ramp.

> F

65) Item Type: Fill-in-the-Blank   Objective: 9-4.4
    Level: I   Tag: None

Energy is transferred as _____ when mechanical energy decreases and temperature increases.

heat

66) Item Type: Essay   Objective: 9-1.1
    Level: II   Tag: None

Three children exhaust themselves trying to push a large rock that doesn't budge. Have they done any work? Why?

Work is defined as force times distance. If the rock has not moved any distance, no work has been done. Work is done only when force causes a change in motion.

67) Item Type: Essay   Objective: 9-1.2
    Level: II   Tag: None

Do machines reduce the amount of work we have to do? If not, why are machines so useful?

A machine does not reduce the amount of work because the work input is always equal to or greater than the work output. Machines enable us to exert smaller forces over greater distances, greater forces over smaller distances, and/or change the direction of force.

68) Item Type: Essay   Objective: 9-2.2
    Level: II   Tag: None

Why does a fixed pulley have a mechanical advantage of 1 and a movable pulley have a mechanical advantage of 2?

When a pulley is stationary, the input distance is equal to the output distance, so the input force must be equal to the output force. When the pulley moves, the input distance is twice as great as the output distance, so the input force is half the output force.

69) Item Type: Essay   Objective: 9-3.2
    Level: II   Tag: None

How does a pendulum show the relationship between gravitational potential energy and kinetic energy?

When a pendulum swings back and forth, it goes from having zero kinetic energy at the top of its path to having a maximum amount of kinetic energy at the bottom of its path. At the same time, it goes from having a maximum amount of gravitational potential energy to having a minimum amount of gravitational potential energy. Energy is changing form back and forth between kinetic energy and gravitational potential energy.

70) Item Type: Essay   Objective: 9-3.5
Level: II   Tag: None

How does a pendulum show that there are nonmechanical forms of energy?

> A pendulum with no external sources of energy will gradually stop swinging because of air resistance, friction, and other forces. Kinetic energy and gravitational potential energy are lost in the system. But because energy is never truly lost, the mechanical energy of the pendulum must be transformed into nonmechanical energy.

71) Item Type: Essay   Objective: 9-3.5
Level: II   Tag: None

What is nuclear fission?

> Nuclear fission is the nuclear reaction that provides the energy for nuclear power plants. Nuclear energy is released when a single heavy nucleus is split into two or more lighter nuclei.

72) Item Type: Essay   Objective: 9-3.5
Level: II   Tag: None

What is nuclear fusion?

> Nuclear fusion is the nuclear reaction that gives the sun its energy. The nuclear energy is released when light atomic nuclei combine to form a heavier nucleus.

73) Item Type: Essay   Objective: 9-3.5
Level: None   Tag: None

Why is light considered a form of energy?

> Light is considered a form of energy because it transforms into other kinds of energy, and other kinds of energy are the source of light. Photosynthesis, for example, converts light energy into chemical energy. In the sun, nuclear energy is converted into light energy. Light is also considered a form of energy because it can do work.

74) Item Type: Essay   Objective: 9-4.1
Level: II   Tag: None

What is the law of conservation of energy?

> The law of conservation of energy states that energy cannot be created or destroyed. This means that when energy transforms from one kind of energy to another, the total amount of energy before the transformation is exactly equal to the amount of energy after the transformation.

75)   Item Type: Essay   Objective: 9-4.2
         Level: II   Tag: None

What is the difference between an open system and a closed system?

> Scientists must carefully define the area or objects they are studying; that is, they must define the system under consideration. If the energy flowing into or out of the system is significant, then the system is open. If the energy flowing into or out of the system is insignificant, the system is said to be closed.

76)   Item Type: Essay   Objective: 9-4.3
         Level: II   Tag: None

What is meant by the efficiency of a machine?

> The work output of a machine is generally less than the work input, because additional force is needed to overcome the effects of friction and other forces. You can measure efficiency by dividing the work output by the work input.

77)   Item Type: Essay   Objective: 9-4.4
         Level: II   Tag: None

Where does energy go when it seems to disappear?

> Because energy can never truly disappear, when it seems to disappear, it is actually being converted into other forms of energy that cannot be observed directly. These may include chemical energy, nuclear energy, potential energy, or even kinetic energy.

1)   Tag Name: Picture of a hand using a pair of tweezers

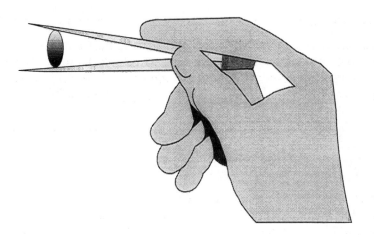

Chapter 10

1) Item Type: Multiple Choice   Objective: 10-1.1
   Level: I   Tag: None

   Temperature is

   a) associated with the   b) proportional to the average
   sensation of hot and cold.   kinetic energy of molecules.

   c) measured with   d) all of the above
   thermometers.

   d

2) Item Type: Multiple Choice   Objective: 10-1.2
   Level: II   Tag: None

   What is 37.0 degrees Celsius on the Fahrenheit scale?

   a) 98.6°F   b) 87.0°F

   c) 92.0°F   d) 102.0°F

   a

3) Item Type: Multiple Choice   Objective: 10-1.2
   Level: II   Tag: None

   What is 175°F on the Celsius scale?

   a) 72.3°C   b) 79.4°C

   c) 84.2°C   d) 92.0°C

   b

4) Item Type: Multiple Choice   Objective: 10-1.2
   Level: II   Tag: None

   What is −175°C on the Kelvin scale?

   a) 76 K   b) 89 K

   c) 98 K   d) 448 K

   c

Chapter 10

5)	Item Type: Multiple Choice	Objective: 10-1.1
	Level: II	Tag: None

As the kinetic energy of the molecules in a substance increases, the

a) temperature of the substance increases.

b) temperature of the substance decreases.

c) potential energy of the substance changes.

d) temperature remains the same.

a

6)	Item Type: Multiple Choice	Objective: 10-2.1
	Level: I	Tag: None

The transfer of energy as heat caused by the collision of molecules is called

a) convection.

b) conduction.

c) contact.

d) radiation.

b

7)	Item Type: Multiple Choice	Objective: 10-2.1
	Level: II	Tag: None

The transfer of energy by the movement of fluids or gases with different temperatures is called

a) convection.

b) conduction.

c) contact.

d) radiation.

a

8)	Item Type: Multiple Choice	Objective: 10-2.1
	Level: II	Tag: None

Energy from the sun reaches Earth by

a) conduction and radiation.

b) radiation only.

c) conduction and convection.

d) conduction only.

b

Chapter 10

9) Item Type: Multiple Choice   Objective: 10-2.1
    Level: II   Tag: None

Convection currents rise in air because

        a) hot air rises and cold air   b) cool air descends and hot
        remains stagnant.   air rises.

        c) the molecules in hot air   d) hot air has less friction.
        move faster.

b

10) Item Type: Multiple Choice   Objective: 10-2.1
    Level: II   Tag: None

Which method of energy transfer does not involve movement of matter?

        a) convection.   b) conduction.

        c) radiation.   d) none of the above.

c

11) Item Type: Multiple Choice   Objective: 10-2.2
    Level: II   Tag: None

Which of the following substances is the best conductor of transferring energy as heat?

        a) carbon dioxide gas   b) water

        c) iron   d) rubber

c

12) Item Type: Multiple Choice   Objective: 10-2.3
    Level: II   Tag: None

Suppose a fixed number of joules of energy as heat is added to 1 kg of the substances listed below. For which substance will the rise in temperature be the least?

        a) liquid ethanol   b) iron

        c) water   d) carbon

c

13) Item Type: Multiple Choice   Objective: 10-2.3
     Level: I   Tag: None

How much heat energy will cause the temperature of 7 kg of carbon to increase its temperature by 15 K? The specific heat of iron is 449 J/kg·K.

     a) 6.8×10^4 J   b) 4.7×10^4 J

     c) 7.0×10^4 J   d) 3.0×10^4 J

b

14) Item Type: Multiple Choice   Objective: 10-3.1
     Level: II   Tag: None

According to the first law of thermodynamics,

     a) there is no such thing as a perpetual motion machine.

     b) the energy of a system is constant.

     c) the total energy used in any process is conserved.

     d) in any process there is a decrease in potential energy.

c

15) Item Type: Multiple Choice   Objective: 10-3.1
     Level: I   Tag: None

Which of the following statements is true?

     a) Energy as heat flows from a lower temperature to a higher temperature.

     b) Energy as heat flows from a higher temperature to a lower temperature.

     c) The amount of heat in a closed system is a constant.

     d) Energy as heat flowing into an object is determined by the amount of work done on the object.

b

16) Item Type: Multiple Choice   Objective: 10-3.1
     Level: II   Tag: None

In an air conditioner, a substance that easily evaporates and condenses is used to transfer energy from a room to the air outside. When the substance evaporates,

a) it absorbs energy as heat from the surrounding air.

b) it transfers energy as heat to the surrounding air.

c) energy is transferred by conduction.

d) energy is transferred by convection.

a

17) Item Type: Multiple Choice   Objective: 10-1.1
     Level: II   Tag: None

The Fahrenheit temperature scale is defined by which of the following temperatures?

a) Water boils at 100 degrees and freezes at 32 degrees.

b) Water boils at 212 degrees and freezes at 32 degrees.

c) Water evaporates at 212 degrees and freezes at 0 degrees.

d) Liquid water turns to a gas at 100 degrees and to a solid at 0 degrees.

b

18) Item Type: Multiple Choice   Objective: 10-3.1
     Level: II   Tag: None

A cold-blooded reptile basks on a warm rock in the sun. Its body is warmed by

a) radiation

b) conduction

c) convection

d) both a and b

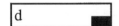

d

19) Item Type: Multiple Choice   Objective: 10-2.3
     Level: II   Tag: None

The temperature of a substance increases by 3 K when 1635 J is added to a 2 kg quantity of the substance. What is the specific heat of the substance?

a) 242 J/kg·K

b) 272 J/kg·K

c) 300 J/kg·K

d) 817 J/kg·K

b

Chapter 10

20) Item Type: Multiple Choice   Objective: 10-2.3
    Level: II   Tag: Table 10-1

Using the table, determine which substance can absorb the most energy in a temperature increase of 1K.

      a) liquid water   b) aluminum

      c) gold   d) lead

a

21) Item Type: Multiple Choice   Objective: 10-2.3
    Level: II   Tag: Table 10-1

Which substance has a specific heat approximately 10 times greater than the specific heat of silver?

      a) water   b) ethanol

      c) carbon   d) mercury

b

22) Item Type: Multiple Choice   Objective: 10-2.3
    Level: II   Tag: Table 10-1

The temperature of 1.5 kg of ethanol is 37°C. What will the final temperature be if 80 000 J of energy as heat is added to the ethanol?

      a) 22°C   b) 51°C

      c) 59°C   d) 67°C

c

23) Item Type: Multiple Choice   Objective: 10-2.3
    Level: II   Tag: Table 10-1

10 kg of a substance underwent a 3 K change in temperature when 11 500 J of energy as heat was added to the substance. What is the substance?

      a) gold   b) water

      c) copper   d) aluminum

c

24) Item Type: True-False   Objective: 10-3.1
    Level: II   Tag: None

In all cooling systems, energy as heat is transferred from one substance to another, leaving the first substance with less energy and with a lower temperature.

T

25) Item Type: True-False   Objective: 10-1.1
    Level: II   Tag: None

All objects produce different types of electromagnetic waves depending on the object's temperature.

| T | ■ |

26) Item Type: True-False   Objective: 10-1.1
    Level: II   Tag: None

As the temperature of mercury inside the thermometer increases, its volume increases.

| T | ■ |

27) Item Type: True-False   Objective: 10-1.2
    Level: II   Tag: None

On the Fahrenheit scale water freezes at $-32°F$.

| F | ■ |

28) Item Type: True-False   Objective: 10-1.2
    Level: II   Tag: None

A degree on the Fahrenheit scale is a bigger unit than a degree on the Celsius scale.

| F | ■ |

29) Item Type: True-False   Objective: 10-1.3
    Level: II   Tag: None

Energy is transferred as heat between two objects at the same temperature.

| F | ■ |

30) Item Type: True-False   Objective: 10-1.3
    Level: II   Tag: None

Energy is transferred as heat from a substance at high temperature to a substance at low temperature.

| T | ■ |

31) Item Type: True-False   Objective: 10-2.1
    Level: III   Tag: None

Heating by convection can occur through solids, liquids, or gases.

| F | ■ |

32) Item Type: True-False   Objective: 10-2.1
    Level: II   Tag: None

Cool objects don't emit any radiation.

| F | ■ |

Chapter 10

33) Item Type: True-False   Objective: 10-2.1
Level: II   Tag: None

Radiation is the only method of energy transfer that can take place in a vacuum.

T

34) Item Type: True-False   Objective: 10-2.1
Level: II   Tag: None

Some substances, when exposed to visible light, absorb more energy as heat than other substances.

T

35) Item Type: True-False   Objective: 10-2.2
Level: II   Tag: None

A good insulator is a poor conductor.

T

36) Item Type: True-False   Objective: 10-2.3
Level: II   Tag: None

How much the temperature of an object increases when energy is transferred as heat to the object depends only on the mass of the object.

F

37) Item Type: Fill-in-the-Blank   Objective: 10-1.1
Level: II   Tag: None

_____ is a measure of the average kinetic energy of all the particles within an object.

Temperature

38) Item Type: Fill-in-the-Blank   Objective: 10-1.1
Level: I   Tag: None

A(n) _____ is a device for measuring temperature.

thermometer

39) Item Type: Fill-in-the-Blank   Objective: 10-1.2
Level: None   Tag: None

_____ is the temperature at which an object's energy is minimal.

Absolute zero

40) Item Type: Fill-in-the-Blank   Objective: 10-1.3
    Level: I   Tag: None

The energy transferred between the particles of two objects because of the temperature difference between the two objects is called _____.

> heat

41) Item Type: Fill-in-the-Blank   Objective: 10-2.1
    Level: I   Tag: None

_____ is the energy transfer as heat between particles as they collide within a substance or between two objects in contact.

> Conduction

42) Item Type: Fill-in-the-Blank   Objective: 10-2.1
    Level: I   Tag: None

_____ is the transfer of energy by the movement of fluids with different temperatures.

> Convection

43) Item Type: Fill-in-the-Blank   Objective: 10-2.1
    Level: I   Tag: None

The movement of a gas or liquid due to expansion and contraction caused by temperature differences within the fluid is called a _____.

> convection current

44) Item Type: Fill-in-the-Blank   Objective: 10-2.1
    Level: I   Tag: None

Radio waves, infrared radiation, visible light, ultraviolet rays, and X rays are forms of _____.

> electromagnetic waves

45) Item Type: Fill-in-the-Blank   Objective: 10-2.1
    Level: I   Tag: None

_____ is the transfer of energy by electromagnetic waves.

> Radiation

46) Item Type: Fill-in-the-Blank   Objective: 10-2.2
    Level: I   Tag: None

A(n) _____ is a material through which energy can be easily transferred as heat.

conductor

47) Item Type: Fill-in-the-Blank   Objective: 10-2.2
    Level: I   Tag: None

A(n) _____ is a material that is a poor energy conductor.

insulator

48) Item Type: Fill-in-the-Blank   Objective: 10-2.3
    Level: II   Tag: None

_____ is the amount of energy transferred as heat that will raise the temperature of 1 kg of a substance by 1 K.

Specific heat

49) Item Type: Fill-in-the-Blank   Objective: 10-3.1
    Level: I   Tag: None

A(n) _____ is any device that transfers energy to a substance to raise the temperature of the substance.

heating system

50) Item Type: Fill-in-the-Blank   Objective: 10-3.1
    Level: II   Tag: None

A(n) _____ is a device that transfers energy out of an object to lower its temperature.

cooling system

51) Item Type: Fill-in-the-Blank   Objective: 10-3.2
    Level: I   Tag: None

A substance used in cooling systems that transfers large amounts of energy as it changes state is called a(n) _____.

refrigerant

52) Item Type: True-False   Objective: 10-2.3
    Level: II   Tag: Table 10-1

It takes more energy as heat to raise the temperature of water by one degree than to raise the temperature of steam by the same amount.

T	▪

53) Item Type: True-False   Objective: 10-3.1
    Level: I   Tag: None

Insulation minimizes undesirable energy transfers.

T	▪

54) Item Type: True-False   Objective: 10-3.1
    Level: I   Tag: None

People feel most comfortable when the temperature of the air is 98.6°F.

F	▪

55) Item Type: True-False   Objective: 10-3.2
    Level: I   Tag: None

The R-value is a standard rating used to measure the effectiveness of insulation.

T	▪

56) Item Type: True-False   Objective: 10-3.2
    Level: II   Tag: None

An active solar heating system needs only sunlight as a source of energy.

F	▪

57) Item Type: True-False   Objective: 10-3.2
    Level: II   Tag: None

The heat exchanger of a heating system uses only convection to transfer energy as heat.

F	▪

58) Item Type: True-False   Objective: 10-3.2
    Level: I   Tag: None

Some of the energy generated as heat by a heating system is always wasted.

T	▪

59) Item Type: True False   Objective: 10-3.2
    Level: I   Tag: Table 10-2

Air is a better insulator than fiberglass batting.

| F |

60) Item Type: True-False   Objective: 10-3.2
    Level: II   Tag: Table 10-2

10 cm of brick is a better insulator than 10 cm of fiberglass batting.

| F |

61) Item Type: True-False   Objective: 10-3.2
    Level: I   Tag: None

The temperature of a volume of gas will change if the pressure of the gas or volume of the gas changes.

| T |

62) Item Type: True-False   Objective: 10-3.2
    Level: II   Tag: None

When a refrigerant evaporates it adds energy as heat to its surroundings.

| F |

63) Item Type: True-False   Objective: 10-3.2
    Level: II   Tag: None

When a refrigerant condenses it gives up energy as heat to its surroundings.

| T |

64) Item Type: Essay   Objective: 10-3.1
    Level: II   Tag: None

Why is the human body like a heating system?

The body must maintain a constant body temperature of about 37°C (98.6°F). If a person is surrounded by cool air, energy will be transferred as heat to the air and the temperature of the skin will drop. Energy is transferred as heat to the skin by the circulation of warm blood. The blood gets energy as heat from body cells that burn nutrients.

65) Item Type: Essay   Objective: 10-3.1
    Level: II   Tag: None

How can work increase the temperature of a substance?

One way is by exerting a force against friction, as you do when you rub your hands together to keep them warm on a cold day. If the force does nothing but overcome friction, all of the work done is converted into energy as heat.

66) Item Type: Essay   Objective: 10-1.1
     Level: II   Tag: None

What is the difference between a thermometer based on a bimetallic strip and a mercury thermometer?

> Most substances expand when heated. In liquid thermometers, the liquid is placed in a long narrow tube, which makes the expansion visible and provides a method for measuring temperature. Metals expand at different rates when heated. In a bimetallic thermometer two different metal strips are welded together. Changes in temperature cause the metal strips to bend because one metal strip expands more than the other metal strip.

67) Item Type: Essay   Objective: 10-1.1
     Level: II   Tag: None

Why do substances expand when energy is added to them as heat?

> Substances and objects are made of particles that are bound together and yet vibrate back and forth. When energy is added as heat, the movement of the particles increases. The greater the movement, the more the substance will expand.

68) Item Type: Essay   Objective: 10-1.2
     Level: II   Tag: None

Why is the lowest possible temperature −273°C?

> At the lowest temperature, which also equals 0 K, the kinetic energy of the particles is minimal and cannot be made any lower. Therefore, the temperature cannot drop any lower.

69) Item Type: Essay   Objective: 10-1.3
     Level: II   Tag: None

What is the connection between heat and temperature?

> Temperature is the measure of the average kinetic energy of all the particles within an object. Heat is the transfer of kinetic energy from the particles of one object to those of another object due to a temperature difference between the two objects.

70) Item Type: Essay   Objective: 10-2.1
     Level: II   Tag: None

Why do rocks in the desert get so hot?

> Rocks in a desert are exposed to sunlight for the entire day. Energy from the sun is absorbed as heat by the rock through radiation.

71) Item Type: Essay   Objective: 10-2.1
    Level: III   Tag: None

At night, a rock in the desert will cool off. How could radiation, convection, and conduction explain how the rock gets colder?

At night, a rock will stop absorbing energy as heat from the sun and start radiating its own energy as heat to the surrounding air, which will have a lower temperature. The rock will lose energy by conduction. Furthermore, a night breeze may blow cool air over the rock, which would be an example of convection.

72) Item Type: Essay   Objective: 10-2.1
    Level: II   Tag: None

How do convection currents form?

When air becomes hot it expands and the air becomes less dense. This decrease in density causes the air to rise. As the air moves up, it cools down, becomes less dense, and sinks. Thus there is a continuous cycle of rising and falling air.

73) Item Type: Essay   Objective: 10-2.1
    Level: II   Tag: None

What is radiation and where does it come from?

Radiation refers to radio waves, infrared radiation, visible light, X rays, and other forms of electromagnetic waves. All objects emit infrared radiation. Radiation from the sun is produced by nuclear fusion, and there are many other different sources of electromagnetic radiation.

74) Item Type: Essay   Objective: 10-2.2
    Level: II   Tag: None

What substances make the best conductors and insulators?

Gas is a very poor conductor because its particles are far apart, which makes the collisions necessary for transferring energy rare. Liquids are naturally better conductors and solids better still. Metals are better conductors than nonmetals. Substances that are poor conductors are good insulators.

75) Item Type: Essay   Objective: 10-2.3
    Level: II   Tag: None

What is specific heat?

Specific heat is the amount of energy as heat required to raise the temperature of 1 kg of a substance by 1°C (or 1 K).

76) Item Type: Essay   Objective: 10-3.1
    Level: II   Tag: None

What is the first law of thermodynamics?

The first law of thermodynamics is the same as the law of conservation of energy. It means that the total energy used in any process is constant.

77) Item Type: Essay   Objective: 10-3.1
    Level: II   Tag: None

Why does energy transferred as heat always move from a higher temperature to a lower temperature?

Energy is transferred as heat because particles with a higher average kinetic energy collide with particles with a lower average kinetic energy. This decreases the average kinetic energy of the particles in the high temperature region and increases the average kinetic energy of the particles in the low temperature region. The result is that energy is transferred from high temperatures to low temperatures.

78) Item Type: Essay   Objective: 10-3.1
    Level: II   Tag: None

How do air conditioners lower the temperature of a room?

Air conditioners use a liquid refrigerant that easily evaporates and condenses. When the liquid evaporates it absorbs energy from the surrounding air, causing the temperature of the surrounding air to drop.

1)   Tag Name: Table 10-1

Specific Heats at 25°C

Substance	c (J/kg•K)	Substance	c (J/kg•K)
Water (liquid)	4186	Copper	385
Steam	1870	Gold	129
Ammonia (gas)	2060	Iron	449
Ethanol (liquid)	2440	Mercury	140
Aluminum	897	Lead	129
Carbon (graphite)	709	Silver	234

2)   Tag Name: Table 10-2

R-Values for Some Common Building Materials

Substance	R-value
Drywall, 1.3 cm (0.50 in.)	0.45
Wood shingles, (overlapping)	0.87
Flat glass, 0.318 cm (0.125 in.)	0.89
Hardwood siding, 2.54 cm (1.00 in.)	0.91
Vertical air space, 8.9 cm (3.5 in.)	1.01
Insulating glass, 0.64 (0.25 in.)	1.54
Cellulose fiber, 2.54 cm (1.00 in.)	3.70
Brick 10.2 cm (4.00 in.)	4.00
Fiberglass batting, 8.9 cm (3.5 in.)	10.90

1)   Item Type: Multiple Choice   Objective: 11-1.1
        Level: I   Tag: None

Sound waves

        a) require a medium.   b) are unrelated to vibrations.

        c) are not mechanical waves.   d) can travel in a vacuum.

a

2)   Item Type: Multiple Choice   Objective: 11-1.2
        Level: II   Tag: None

Light waves

        a) require a medium.   b) cannot travel through
                                        solids.

        c) are caused by a vibrating   d) are electromagnetic waves.
        object.

d

3)   Item Type: Multiple Choice   Objective: 11-1.1
        Level: II   Tag: None

Water waves

        a) transport energy and water. b) transport energy but not
                                        water.

        c) transport water but not   d) are not mechanical waves.
        energy.

b

4)   Item Type: Multiple Choice   Objective: 11-1.1
        Level: II   Tag: None

The medium seismic waves travel through is

        a) a vacuum.   b) rocks and other materials inside Earth.

        c) air.   d) energy.

b

5) Item Type: Multiple Choice   Objective: 11-1.4
   Level: II   Tag: None

Sound waves are

    a) transverse waves.   b) longitudinal waves.

    c) circular waves.   d) polarized waves.

b

6) Item Type: Multiple Choice   Objective: 11-1.4
   Level: II   Tag: None

Light waves are

    a) transverse waves.   b) longitudinal waves.

    c) rotating waves.   d) circular waves.

a

7) Item Type: Multiple Choice   Objective: 11-1.4
   Level: II   Tag: None

Water waves are

    a) longitudinal waves.   b) transverse waves.

    c) mechanical waves.   d) compression waves.

c

8) Item Type: Multiple Choice   Objective: 11-2.1
   Level: II   Tag: Specification #1

The wavelength of the wave in the diagram is

    a) 6.0 m.   b) 1.5 m.

    c) 3 m.   d) 0.75 m.

b

9) Item Type: Multiple Choice   Objective: 11-2.1
   Level: II   Tag: Specification #1

The amplitude of the above wave is

    a) 6 m.   b) 3 m.

    c) 0.5 m.   d) 1 m.

c

10) Item Type: Multiple Choice   Objective: 11-2.2
Level: II   Tag: None

A wave has a period of 0.25 seconds. The frequency of this wave is

    a) 25 seconds.   b) 0.25 hertz.

    c) 4 hertz.   d) 2 hertz.

c

11) Item Type: Multiple Choice   Objective: 11-2.2
Level: II   Tag: None

A man is standing on the shore of a beach, up to his knees in water. Every 5 seconds a wave breaks on him. What is the period of the wave?

    a) 12 waves per minute   b) 5 hertz

    c) 5 seconds   d) 0.2 hertz

c

12) Item Type: Multiple Choice   Objective: 11-2.3
Level: II   Tag: None

A child is sending pulses down a stretched rope at a rate of 2 pulses per second. The distance between the pulses is 5 meters. What is the speed of the wave?

    a) 5 m/s   b) 10 m/s

    c) 2 Hz   d) 2.5 m/s

b

13) Item Type: Multiple Choice   Objective: 11-2.3
Level: II   Tag: None

A train of waves is moving at a speed of 30 m/s. The frequency of the waves is 10 Hz. What is the wavelength?

    a) 300 m   b) 30 m

    c) 3 m   d) 0.1 m

c

14) Item Type: Multiple Choice   Objective: 11-2.3
    Level: III   Tag: None

A sound wave in air has a frequency of 680 cycles per second. What is the approximate wavelength of the sound wave?

    a) 680 m   b) 0.5 m

    c) 340 m   d) 20 m

b

15) Item Type: Multiple Choice   Objective: 11-2.4
    Level: I   Tag: None

A person is standing still and listening to a siren sounding an alarm. The frequency of the sound is 500 Hz. The person begins running toward the sound at a rate of 20 m/s. The frequency of the sound the person hears will

    a) remain the same.   b) increase.

    c) decrease.   d) change by 20 Hz.

b

16) Item Type: Multiple Choice   Objective: 11-1.1
    Level: II   Tag: None

A wavefront is

    a) the first part of a wave.   b) a surface made up of all the points on a wave that have the same energy.

    c) a line connecting a crest and a trough.   d) the initial disturbance of the medium.

b

17) Item Type: Multiple Choice   Objective: 11-2.2
    Level: II   Tag: None

The frequency of a sound wave determines

    a) the pitch of the sound.   b) how loud the sound is.

    c) how fast the sound travels.   d) the magnitude of the compression.

a

Chapter 11

18) Item Type: Multiple Choice   Objective: 11-2.2
    Level: II   Tag: None

How loud a sound is depends on

    a) the wavelength of the sound. b) the pitch of the sound.

    c) the amplitude of the waves. d) the medium.

c

19) Item Type: Multiple Choice   Objective: 11-2.2
    Level: II   Tag: None

The difference between visible light and X rays is that

    a) the amplitude of visible   b) the speed of X rays is
    light is greater.   greater.

    c) they travel through a   d) the frequency of X rays is
    different medium.   greater.

d

20) Item Type: Multiple Choice   Objective: 11-2.1
    Level: II   Tag: None

A _____ is a good mathematical model for representing transverse waves.

    a) tangent curve   b) sine curve

    c) exponential curve   d) parabolic curve

b

21) Item Type: Multiple Choice   Objective: 11-2.2
    Level: II   Tag: None

The color of light is determined by _____ of the light waves.

    a) the medium   b) the speed

    c) the frequency   d) the amplitude

c

22) Item Type: Multiple Choice   Objective: 11-2.2
    Level: II   Tag: None

Which type of electromagnetic wave has the greatest wavelength?

    a) visible light   b) microwaves

    c) radio waves   d) X rays

c

23) Item Type: Multiple Choice   Objective: 11-2.2
     Level: II   Tag: None

The frequency of a sound wave is determined by the

   a) source of the wave.   b) amplitude of the wave.

   c) speed of the wave.   d) medium of the wave.

a

24) Item Type: Multiple Choice   Objective: 11-2.3
     Level: III   Tag: None

A wave *x* meters long has a speed of *y* meters per second. The frequency of the wave is

   a) x/y b) y/x

   c) $y \bullet x$ d) $y + x$

b

25) Item Type: Multiple Choice   Objective: 11-2.3
     Level: II   Tag: None

A wave with a frequency of 0.5 Hz and a speed of 10 m/s has a wavelength of

   a) 50 m.   b) 0.5 m.

   c) 20 m.   d) 0.2 m.

c

26) Item Type: True-False   Objective: 11-2.1
     Level: II   Tag: None

The greater the frequency of the wave in a particular medium, the greater the speed of the wave.

F

27) Item Type: True-False   Objective: 11-2.3
     Level: II   Tag: None

Light travels faster in glass than it does in a vacuum.

F

28) Item Type: True-False   Objective: 11-1.1
     Level: II   Tag: None

A wave transports energy but not matter.

T

29) Item Type: True-False   Objective: 11-1.2
    Level: II   Tag: None

Visible light waves require a medium in which to travel.

F

30) Item Type: True-False   Objective: 11-1.2
    Level: II   Tag: None

Radio waves are an example of electromagnetic waves.

T

31) Item Type: True-False   Objective: 11-1.4
    Level: II   Tag: None

Sound waves are examples of longitudinal waves.

T

32) Item Type: True-False   Objective: 11-1.4
    Level: II   Tag: None

Light waves are examples of transverse waves.

T

33) Item Type: True-False   Objective: 11-2.1
    Level: II   Tag: None

The energy of a mechanical wave depends on the amplitude of the wave.

T

34) Item Type: True-False   Objective: 11-2.2
    Level: II   Tag: None

As the frequency of sound waves increases, the wavelength of the sound waves decreases.

T

35) Item Type: True-False   Objective: 11-2.3
    Level: II   Tag: None

As the period of a wave increases, the frequency increases.

F

36) Item Type: True-False   Objective: 11-2.3
    Level: II   Tag: None

In water waves, the disturbance consists of fluctuations in the density of water.

F

37) Item Type: True-False   Objective: 11-2.3
Level: III   Tag: None

The speed of sound at high altitudes, where the air is less dense, is greater than the speed of sound at low altitudes, where the air is more dense.

| F |

38) Item Type: True-False   Objective: 11-2.3
Level: II   Tag: None

The color of visible light depends on the wavelength of the light.

| T |

39) Item Type: Fill-in-the-Blank   Objective: 11-1.1
Level: II   Tag: None

A(n) _____ is a disturbance that transmits energy through matter or space.

| wave |

40) Item Type: Fill-in-the-Blank   Objective: 11-1.1
Level: I   Tag: None

The matter through which a wave travels is called the _____.

| medium |

41) Item Type: Fill-in-the-Blank   Objective: 11-1.2
Level: I   Tag: None

A(n) _____ is defined as a wave that requires a medium.

| mechanical wave |

42) Item Type: Fill-in-the-Blank   Objective: 11-1.2
Level: I   Tag: None

A(n) _____ consists of changing electric and magnetic fields and does not require a medium.

| electromagnetic wave |

43) Item Type: Fill-in-the-Blank   Objective: None
Level: None   Tag: None

A wave that causes the particles of the medium to vibrate perpendicularly to the direction the wave travels is called a(n) _____.

| transverse wave |

44) Item Type: Fill-in-the-Blank   Objective: 11-1.4
    Level: I   Tag: None

A wave that causes the particles of the medium to vibrate parallel to the direction the wave travels is called a(n) _____.

| longitudinal wave ■ |

45) Item Type: Fill-in-the-Blank   Objective: 11-2.1
    Level: I   Tag: None

The highest point of a transverse wave is called the _____.

| crest ■ |

46) Item Type: Fill-in-the-Blank   Objective: 11-2.1
    Level: I   Tag: None

The lowest point of a transverse wave is called the _____.

| trough ■ |

47) Item Type: Fill-in-the-Blank   Objective: 11-2.1
    Level: I   Tag: None

The _____ is the greatest distance that particles in a medium move from their normal position when a wave passes.

| amplitude ■ |

48) Item Type: Fill-in-the-Blank   Objective: 11-2.2
    Level: I   Tag: None

The _____ is the time required for one full wavelength to pass a certain point.

| period ■ |

49) Item Type: Fill-in-the-Blank   Objective: 11-2.2
    Level: I   Tag: None

The _____ is the number of vibrations that occur in a 1-second time interval.

| frequency ■ |

50) Item Type: Fill-in-the-Blank   Objective: 11-3.1
    Level: II   Tag: None

The bouncing back of a wave as it meets a surface or boundary is called _____.

| reflection ■ |

51) Item Type: Fill-in-the-Blank   Objective: 11-3.1
    Level: I   Tag: None

The bending of a wave as it passes an edge or an opening is called _____.

| diffraction |

52) Item Type: Fill-in-the-Blank   Objective: 11-3.1
    Level: I   Tag: None

The bending of waves as they pass from one medium to another is called

_____.

| refraction |

53) Item Type: Fill-in-the-Blank   Objective: 11-3.2
    Level: I   Tag: None

_____ occurs when two or more waves exist in the same place at the same time.

| Interference |

54) Item Type: Fill-in-the-Blank   Objective: 11-3.3
    Level: I   Tag: None

In _____, waves combine so that the resulting wave is smaller than the largest of the original waves.

| destructive interference |

55) Item Type: Fill-in-the-Blank   Objective: 11-3.3
    Level: I   Tag: None

In _____, waves combine so that the resulting wave is bigger than the largest of the original waves.

| constructive interference |

56) Item Type: Fill-in-the-Blank   Objective: 11-3.4
    Level: I   Tag: None

A(n) _____ is a wave form caused by interference that appears not to move along the medium and that shows nodes and antinodes.

| standing wave |

57) Item Type: True-False   Objective: 11-2.1
    Level: II   Tag: None

Sound waves cannot travel through solids.

| F |

58) Item Type: True-False   Objective: 11-3.1
    Level: II   Tag: None

When a wave reflects from a boundary, the only change in the wave is the direction of travel.

F

59) Item Type: True-False   Objective: 11-2.4
    Level: III   Tag: None

According to the Doppler effect, light from a star moving away from Earth will have a higher frequency than light from a star moving toward Earth.

F

60) Item Type: True-False   Objective: 11-3.2
    Level: II   Tag: None

When two waves are in the same place at the same time, they combine to produce a single wave.

T

61) Item Type: True-False   Objective: 11-3.2
    Level: II   Tag: None

Two waves cannot occupy the same space at the same time.

F

62) Item Type: True-False   Objective: 11-3.3
    Level: II   Tag: None

Nodes in a standing wave are the result of constructive interference.

F

63) Item Type: True-False   Objective: 11-3.3
    Level: I   Tag: None

If two tuning forks of different frequencies are struck at the same time, you will hear beats as the result of constructive interference followed by destructive interference.

T

64) Item Type: True-False   Objective: 11-3.3
    Level: II   Tag: None

When light passes from air to glass, the light may change direction due to refraction.

T

Chapter 11

65) Item Type: Essay　　　　　　　　Objective: 11-1.1
　　Level: II　　　　　　　　　　　Tag: None

What is the primary difference between an object moving at 5 m/s and a mechanical wave moving at 5 m/s?

> The object itself is moving at 5 m/s. In the case of the wave, there is no matter that is moving at 5 m/s. What is moving at this rate is a disturbance of the medium.

66) Item Type: Essay　　　　　　　　Objective: 11-1.1
　　Level: II　　　　　　　　　　　Tag: None

Explain the difference between mechanical waves and electromagnetic waves.

> Mechanical waves require a medium in which to travel. Electromagnetic waves do not.

67) Item Type: Essay　　　　　　　　Objective: 11-1.3
　　Level: II　　　　　　　　　　　Tag: None

Explain the relationship between vibrations and waves.

> Most waves are caused by a vibrating object. Mechanical waves are caused by the vibrating particles of the medium. Electromagnetic waves may be caused by vibrating charged particles.

68) Item Type: Essay　　　　　　　　Objective: 11-1.1
　　Level: II　　　　　　　　　　　Tag: None

When a rock is thrown into water, causing a wave, will the wave ever completely disappear?

> Yes. The initial energy of the wave will eventually be absorbed by the water and transferred into a different form of energy.

69) Item Type: Essay　　　　　　　　Objective: 11-2.2
　　Level: II　　　　　　　　　　　Tag: None

What is the electromagnetic spectrum and what types of waves are included in the spectrum?

> The electromagnetic spectrum refers to the full range of electromagnetic waves arranged from low frequency to high frequency, or long wavelength to short wavelength. The types of electromagnetic waves, starting at the low frequency end of the spectrum, are radio waves, microwaves, infrared light, visible light, ultraviolet light, X rays, and gamma rays.

70) Item Type: Essay   Objective: 11-2.1
    Level: II   Tag: None

Contrast the amplitude of a transverse wave with the amplitude of a longitudinal wave.

> For a transverse wave, the motion of the particles of the medium is perpendicular to the direction the energy of the wave travels in. The amplitude refers to the maximum distance the particles move. In longitudinal waves, the motion of the particles is in the same direction as the direction the energy of the wave moves in. This generates areas of rarefaction and compression, or areas of high particle density and areas of low particle density. The amplitude of a longitudinal wave generally refers to differences in density or pressure.

71) Item Type: Essay   Objective: 11-2.2
    Level: III   Tag: None

In the case of mechanical waves, what causes or determines the speed of the waves, the frequency of the waves, and the wavelengths of the waves?

> The speed of the wave is determined by the characteristics of the medium. The frequency of the wave is determined by the source of the wave. For example, if the frequency of a sound wave in air is 550 Hz, it is because a tuning fork or guitar string is vibrating 550 times per second. The medium and the frequency then determine the wavelength in accordance with the wave speed equation.

72) Item Type: Essay   Objective: 11-2.1
    Level: II   Tag: None

Why does sound travel faster in solids than in liquids, and faster in liquids than in gases?

> When a particle of a medium is disturbed, it will cause a neighboring particle to be disturbed. The closer the particles are and the more tightly they are bound, the faster the disturbance will travel through the medium. The particles of solids are very close together, the particles of liquids are not as close, and the particles of a gas are relatively far away from each other.

73) Item Type: Essay   Objective: 11-2.1
    Level: II   Tag: None

Suppose ocean waves are hitting a shore at a frequency of 20 waves per minute. Two swimmers are in the water. One swimmer says the frequency is 25 waves per minute and the other says the frequency is 15 waves per minute. How can the Doppler effect explain this apparent difference?

> One swimmer is swimming out to sea and is moving against the direction the waves are traveling, which causes the swimmer to encounter a wave 25 times per minute. The other swimmer is swimming toward shore in the same direction the waves are traveling, so that swimmer encounters waves less frequently.

74) | Item Type: Essay | Objective: 11-2.1
Level: II | Tag: None

Compare and contrast refraction and reflection.

Both refraction and reflection occur when a wave traveling through a medium encounters a different medium. Reflection involves the wave bouncing back into the original medium, while refraction involves the wave changing direction as it passes into the new medium.

75) | Item Type: Essay | Objective: 11-2.2
Level: II | Tag: None

What causes the colorful swirls in soap bubbles?

The interference of light waves. Some waves bounce directly off the outer surface of the bubble, while, some waves travel through the bubble, then bounce off the inner surface of the bubble. The constructive and destructive interference of these different sets of light waves produce different colors.

76) | Item Type: Essay | Objective: 11-3.2
Level: II | Tag: None

What happens when two waves are in the same place at the same time?

A wave is not an object but a disturbance that is propagated through a medium. For this reason, it is possible for two different waves to occupy the same space at the same time. When they do, a single wave is formed. This is called interference.

77) | Item Type: Essay | Objective: 11-3.2
Level: II | Tag: None

What determines whether the interference between two waves is constructive or destructive?

If the motion of the particles of the two waves are in the same direction at a given point, the motions will add up and there will be constructive interference. Otherwise, there will be destructive interference.

78) | Item Type: Essay | Objective: 11-3.1
Level: II | Tag: None

Explain how two sound waves of slightly different frequencies produce beats.

When the two different sound waves are added together, there is alternating destructive and constructive interference. Constructive interference causes the loudness of the sound to increase and destructive interference causes the loudness to decrease.

1)   Tag Name: Specification #1

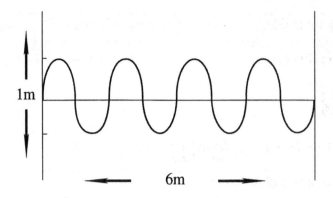

Chapter 12

1) Item Type: Multiple Choice   Objective: 12-1.1
    Level: I   Tag: None

Sound travels fastest in

    a) air at 0° C.   b) air at 25° C.

    c) rubber.   d) sea water.

    d

2) Item Type: Multiple Choice   Objective: 12-1.2
    Level: I   Tag: None

The intensity of a sound describes

    a) its speed.   b) its loudness at a particular
                                       distance.

    c) the distance and medium   d) the medium through which
       through which it travels   it travels.

    b

3) Item Type: Multiple Choice   Objective: 12-1.2
    Level: I   Tag: None

The pitch of a sound is most closely related to the

    a) frequency of vibrations.   b) distance from the sound
                                       source.

    c) medium through which the   d) intensity of the sound.
       sound travels.

    a

4) Item Type: Multiple Choice   Objective: 12-1.3
    Level: I   Tag: None

The unique sound quality of a clarinet or a violin is caused by the

    a) forced vibrations that occur   b) length of standing waves in
       at natural frequencies.   the fundamental frequency.

    c) relative intensity of different d) relative number of
       harmonics in each note.   harmonics.

    c

Chapter 12

5) Item Type: Multiple Choice   Objective: 12-1.3
   Level: I   Tag: None

Resonance refers to an effect in which the

a) vibration of one object   b) intensity of a sound
causes another object to   decreases over time.
vibrate at natural frequencies.

c) pitch of a note is compared   d) vibration of a string or
to a pure tone.   column of air causes a
                                    standing wave at a natural
                                    frequency.

a

6) Item Type: Multiple Choice   Objective: 12-1.4
   Level: I   Tag: None

When a sound wave strikes your eardrum, it causes forced vibrations that are transferred
to the

a) brain.   b) outer ear.

c) longitudinal canal.   d) hammer, anvil, and stirrup.

d

7) Item Type: Multiple Choice   Objective: 12-1.4
   Level: I   Tag: None

The structure within the cochlea containing hair cells that vibrate at different natural
frequencies is the

a) eardrum.   b) basilar membrane.

c) inner ear.   d) hammer and anvil.

b

8) Item Type: Multiple Choice   Objective: 12-1.5
   Level: I   Tag: None

A sonar system measures distance by determining the

a) density of a body of water.   b) time it takes for sound to
                                    be absorbed.

c) difference between regular   d) time it takes for sound
sound waves and ultrasound.   waves to bounce off a surface.

d

Chapter 12

9) Item Type: Multiple Choice   Objective: 12-1.5
    Level: I   Tag: None

An ultrasound system can produce images of body structures because sound waves

       a) travel only in straight lines.   b) travel at different speeds
                                       through materials of different
                                       densities.

       c) cannot pass through liquids   d) increase their speed and
       or gaseous materials.   change their direction as they
                                         leave the body.

b

10) Item Type: Multiple Choice   Objective: 12-2.1
    Level: I   Tag: None

Which property of light is *not* explained by the wave model of light?

       a) Light produces interference   b) Light is diffracted when it
       patterns.   passes through a narrow
                                         opening.

       c) Blue light can knock   d) Light reflects when it
       electrons off a plate but red   meets a mirror, but it refracts
       light cannot.   when it passes through a
                                         lens.

c

11) Item Type: Multiple Choice   Objective: 12-2.1
    Level: I   Tag: None

The particle model of light explains how light can

       a) travel through empty space   b) refract when it passes
       without a medium.   through a lens.

       c) be reflected off a mirror.   d) diffract when it passes
                                      through a normal opening.

a

12) Item Type: Multiple Choice   Objective: 12-2.2
    Level: I   Tag: None

The amount of energy in a photon of light is proportional to the

a) medium through which it travels.

b) shape of the light wave it creates.

c) speed of the corresponding light wave.

d) frequency of the corresponding light wave.

d

13) Item Type: Multiple Choice   Objective: 12-2.2
    Level: I   Tag: None

The rate at which light energy flows through a given area of space is referred to as its

a) speed.

b) wavelength.

c) intensity.

d) energy.

c

14) Item Type: Multiple Choice   Objective: 12-2.3
    Level: I   Tag: None

Which type of electromagnetic waves has slightly longer wavelengths than red light?

a) yellow light

b) infrared light

c) ultraviolet light

d) green light

b

15) Item Type: Multiple Choice   Objective: 12-2.3
    Level: I   Tag: None

Which type of waves has wavelengths longer than microwaves?

a) infrared

b) visible light

c) radio waves

d) gamma rays

c

Chapter 12

16) Item Type: Multiple Choice   Objective: 12-2.3
    Level: I   Tag: None

Which type of electromagnetic waves has the highest frequency?

        a) gamma rays   b) ultraviolet light

        c) infrared   d) microwaves

a

17) Item Type: Multiple Choice   Objective: 12-2.4
    Level: I   Tag: None

Which type of electromagnetic radiation is used to kill cancer cells?

        a) microwaves   b) gamma rays

        c) ultraviolet rays   d) sunlight

b

18) Item Type: Multiple Choice   Objective: 12-2.4
    Level: I   Tag: None

Short-range radar works by sending a signal out from a control tower that is

    a) analyzed by a Doppler scanner on the ground.   b) reflected off a plane back to the control tower.

    c) increased in intensity as it passes through the atmosphere.   d) scanned and analyzed by a receiver on board an airplane.

b

19) Item Type: Multiple Choice   Objective: 12-3.1
    Level: I   Tag: None

When light rays reflect off a rough surface, they

    a) scatter in many different directions.   b) converge toward the normal.

    c) diverge away from the normal.   d) decrease their speed and change their angle.

a

Chapter 12

20) Item Type: Multiple Choice   Objective: 12-3.2
    Level: I   Tag: None

The law of reflection states that when light rays reflect off a surface the angle of incidence

a) is one-half the angle of reflection.

b) equals the angle of reflection.

c) is twice the angle of reflection.

d) equals the angle of refraction.

b

21) Item Type: Multiple Choice   Objective: 12-3.2
    Level: I   Tag: ES-6

Which drawing illustrates the law of reflection?

c

22) Item Type: Multiple Choice   Objective: 12-3.3
    Level: I   Tag: None

An image that results from an apparent path of light rays is called

a) an apparent image.

b) a real image.

c) an objective image.

d) a virtual image.

d

23) Item Type: Multiple Choice   Objective: 12-3.3
    Level: I   Tag: None

Which statement about mirrors is *incorrect*?

a) Flat mirrors create virtual images.

b) Concave mirrors can create real or virtual images.

c) Curved mirrors distort images by reflecting light according to the law of reflection.

d) Only convex mirrors work according to the law of reflection.

d

24) Item Type: Multiple Choice   Objective: 12-3.5
    Level: II   Tag: None

An orange looks orange because it

a) reflects orange light and   b) absorbs orange light and
absorbs other colors.   reflects other colors.

c) reflects red and yellow light   d) absorbs red and yellow
only.   light only.

a

25) Item Type: Multiple Choice   Objective: 12-3.5
    Level: II   Tag: None

You look at a red tulip, with green leaves, under green light. What would you see?

a) a green flower with green   b) a black flower with green
leaves   leaves

c) a yellow flower with black   d) a black flower with black
leaves   leaves

b

26) Item Type: Multiple Choice   Objective: 12-3.4
    Level: I   Tag: None

The color that an object appears to be depends on the

a) angle at which visible light   b) use of additive rather than
is reflected off the object.   subtractive colors.

c) wavelengths of light that the   d) speed with which visible
object reflects.   light reaches it.

c

27) Item Type: Multiple Choice   Objective: 12-4.1
    Level: II   Tag: None

When light moves from a material in which its speed is higher to a material in which its speed is lower, it is

        a) bent toward the normal.   b) bent away from the normal.

        c) reflected off the boundary.   d) changed into a virtual image.

a

28) Item Type: Multiple Choice   Objective: 12-4.1
    Level: I   Tag: None

A virtual image caused by reflection of light in the atmosphere is called

        a) a prism.   b) a lens.

        c) a mirror.   d) a mirage.

d

29) Item Type: Multiple Choice   Objective: 12-4.2
    Level: II   Tag: None

Light that enters one end of a fiber optic cable reaches the other end by means of

        a) dispersion.   b) magnification.

        c) repeated intensification.   d) total internal reflection.

d

30) Item Type: Multiple Choice   Objective: 12-4.3
Level: II   Tag: None

Which statement about a diverging lens is correct?

a) It bends light inward and can create either a virtual or a real image.

b) It bends light inward and can only create a real image.

c) It bends light outward and can create either a virtual or a real image.

d) It bends light outward and can only create a virtual image.

d

31) Item Type: Multiple Choice   Objective: 12-4.3
Level: I   Tag: None

Light rays that pass through a lens change direction because

a) each light ray strikes the curved surface at a different angle.

b) they are refracted.

c) light is broken up into many different colors.

d) virtual images always appear slightly larger than real images.

b

32) Item Type: Multiple Choice   Objective: 12-4.4
Level: II   Tag: None

Which statement about the lens of the eye is *incorrect*?

a) It is made of glassy fibers.

b) It is behind the iris.

c) It has a fixed curvature.

d) It focuses light rays on the retina.

c

33) Item Type: Multiple Choice   Objective: 12-4.4
    Level: II   Tag: None

Which structure within the eye is responsible for the largest percentage of refraction of light?

        a) retina   b) cornea

        c) lens   d) iris

b

34) Item Type: Multiple Choice   Objective: 12-4.5
    Level: I   Tag: None

The effect in which white light separates into different colors is called

        a) magnification.   b) refraction.

        c) reflection.   d) dispersion.

d

35) Item Type: Multiple Choice   Objective: 12-4.5
    Level: II   Tag: None

White light breaks up into different colors when it passes through a prism because of

        a) differences in wave speed.   b) total internal dispersion.

        c) a combination of refraction   d) droplets in the air.
        and reflection.

a

36) Item Type: Short Answer   Objective: 12-1.1
    Level: I   Tag: None

In a gas, such as air, an increase in temperature results in a(n) _____ in the speed of sound.

increase

37) Item Type: Short Answer   Objective: 12-1.2
    Level: I   Tag: None

The greater the _____ of a sound wave, the louder the sound.

amplitude

38) Item Type: Short Answer   Objective: 12-1.2
    Level: I   Tag: None

A high-pitched sound results when a string or a column of air _____.

vibrates rapidly

39) Item Type: Short Answer   Objective: 12-1.3
    Level: II   Tag: None

The note A-natural sounds different on a tuning fork, a violin, and a flute because of the relative amplitudes of _____.

harmonics

40) Item Type: Short Answer   Objective: 12-1.3
    Level: II   Tag: None

Resonance occurs when the vibration of one object causes another object to vibrate at a(n) _____.

natural frequency

41) Item Type: Short Answer   Objective: 12-1.4
    Level: I   Tag: None

The three small bones in your middle ear are the _____, the _____, and the _____.

hammer; anvil; stirrup

42) Item Type: Short Answer   Objective: 12-1.4
    Level: II   Tag: None

In your inner ear, different parts of the _____ vibrate at different natural frequencies.

basilar membrane (or cochlea)

43) Item Type: Short Answer   Objective: 12-1.5
    Level: 1   Tag: None

Sound waves with frequencies higher than 20 000 Hz are referred to as _____ waves.

> ultrasound

44) Item Type: Short Answer   Objective: 12-2.1
    Level: 1   Tag: None

Sonograms are possible because some ultrasound waves are _____ when they pass from one type of material to another.

> reflected

45) Item Type: Short Answer   Objective: 12-2.1
    Level: 1   Tag: None

The two most common models of light describe it as a wave or as a stream of _____.

> particles

46) Item Type: Short Answer   Objective: 12-2.1
    Level: 1   Tag: None

In the particle model of light, individual "packets" of light are called _____.

> photons

47) Item Type: Short Answer   Objective: 12-2.2
    Level: 1   Tag: None

The energy of light is proportional to the _____ of the corresponding _____.

> frequency; light wave

48) Item Type: Short Answer   Objective: 12-2.2
    Level: 1   Tag: None

The amount of light that illuminates a given surface area is referred to as _____.

> intensity

49) Item Type: Short Answer   Objective: 12-2.1
     Level: II   Tag: None

In a vacuum, all light travels at the same speed, which is _____.

3×10^8 m/s or 186 000 mi/s

50) Item Type: Short Answer   Objective: 12-2.3
     Level: I   Tag: None

All possible kinds of light, at all energies, frequencies, and wavelengths, make up the _____.

electromagnetic spectrum

51) Item Type: Short Answer   Objective: 12-2.3
     Level: I   Tag: None

The electromagnetic waves with the highest energy and shortest wavelengths are classified as _____.

gamma rays

52) Item Type: Short Answer   Objective: 12-2.4
     Level: I   Tag: None

_____ are used for cooking as well as for communication.

Microwaves

53) Item Type: Short Answer   Objective: 12-2.4
     Level: II   Tag: None

A(n) _____ sensor can be used to measure the heat that objects radiate.

infrared

54) Item Type: Short Answer   Objective: 12-3.1
     Level: II   Tag: None

Reflection of light into random directions is called _____ reflection.

diffuse

55) Item Type: Short Answer   Objective: 12-3.1
       Level: II   Tag: None

The theoretical line perpendicular to the surface where light hits a mirror is called the

_____.

normal

56) Item Type: Short Answer   Objective: 12-3.2
       Level: I   Tag: None

The law of reflection states that the angle of _____ is the same as the angle of

_____.

incidence; reflection

57) Item Type: Short Answer   Objective: 12-3.3
       Level: I   Tag: None

The image that you see in a mirror that results from the apparent path of light rays is
called a(n) _____ image.

virtual

58) Item Type: Short Answer   Objective: 12-3.3
       Level: I   Tag: None

In a(n) _____ image, light rays really exist at the point where the image
appears.

real

59) Item Type: Short Answer   Objective: 12-3.4
       Level: II   Tag: None

Colors that combine to produce white are called _____ colors.

additive

60) Item Type: Short Answer   Objective: 12-3.4
       Level: III   Tag: None

Colors that combine to create magenta, cyan, or yellow are called _____ colors.

primary subtractive

61) Item Type: Short Answer   Objective: 12-3.5
    Level: 1   Tag: None

An object looks red if it _____ red light and _____ all other colors.

| reflects; absorbs | ■ |

62) Item Type: Short Answer   Objective: 12-3.5
    Level: 1   Tag: None

White light actually contains all the visible wavelengths of the _____.

| electromagnetic spectrum | ■ |

63) Item Type: Short Answer   Objective: 12-4.1
    Level: 1   Tag: None

Light may bend when it changes mediums because _____ is different in each medium.

| the speed of light | ■ |

64) Item Type: Short Answer   Objective: 12-4.1
    Level: 1   Tag: None

If a light moves from a material in which its speed is lower to one in which its speed is higher, the ray is bent away from the _____.

| normal | ■ |

65) Item Type: Short Answer   Objective: 12-4.2
    Level: II   Tag: None

Light inside a fiber optic cable bounces off the walls of the fiber because of _____ reflection.

| total internal | ■ |

66) Item Type: Short Answer   Objective: 12-4.3
    Level: 1   Tag: None

A lens that bends light inward is called a(n) _____ lens.

| converging | ■ |

67) Item Type: Short Answer   Objective: 12-4.3
    Level: I   Tag: None

A lens that bends light outward is called a(n) _____ lens.

diverging

68) Item Type: Short Answer   Objective: 12-4.4
    Level: II   Tag: None

Light first enters the eye through a transparent tissue called the _____.

cornea

69) Item Type: Short Answer   Objective: 12-4.4
    Level: II   Tag: None

The cone cells in the eye allow _____ vision, and the rod cells are more sensitive to _____ light.

color; dim

70) Item Type: Short Answer   Objective: 12-4.5
    Level: I   Tag: None

A transparent object that can separate white light into different colors is called a(n) _____.

prism

71) Item Type: Short Answer   Objective: 12-4.5
    Level: I   Tag: None

The effect in which light separates into different colors because of differences in speed is called _____.

dispersion

72) Item Type: Essay   Objective: 12-1.3
    Level: III   Tag: None

Explain how the basilar membrane, which is located inside the cochlea in the inner ear, uses resonance to help you hear.

The basilar membrane has many hair cells, each of which vibrates at a different natural frequency. As waves pass through the cochlea, they resonate with different hair cells, simulating nerve fibers that send impulses to the brain. The brain interprets each impulse as a different sound frequency.

73) Item Type: Essay   Objective: 12-1.2
     Level: III   Tag: None

Explain how musical instruments rely on the principles of harmonics to produce a wide variety of sounds.

> A violin string or the air column inside a flute vibrate not only at a fundamental frequency but also at certain whole-number multiples of that frequency called harmonics. Thus an instrument actually produces many different tones simultaneously, and the particular harmonic pattern gives each type of instrument a unique sound quality.

74) Item Type: Essay   Objective: 12-2.1
     Level: III   Tag: None

What does it mean to say that light can be modeled as both a wave and particle? Explain the implications for scientific theory.

> Scientific theories are successful to the extent that they explain observations. Some observations are best explained by a wave model of light. Other observations are best explained by a particle model. Therefore, both models are currently accepted as correct and light is considered to have a dual nature.

75) Item Type: Essay   Objective: 12-2.4
     Level: II   Tag: None

Describe two different forms of electromagnetic radiation and explain their use in technology.

> Answers will vary. X rays, with high energy and short wavelengths, are used to produce images of the body's interior; infrared, with wavelengths longer than red light, can be used to keep food warm; microwaves, with still longer wavelengths, can be used for cooking and for communication; radio waves, with the longest wavelengths, can be used in communication and radar.

76) Item Type: Essay   Objective: 12-3.1
     Level: III   Tag: None

Why do scientists use a third model of light, the light ray, in addition to the wave and particle models? How are the three models connected?

> The light ray, an imaginary straight line that shows how light travels, is a useful tool for describing the way we experience light in everyday life. It is the same as the direction of wave travel in the wave model or the path of photons in the particle model.

77)   Item Type: Essay   Objective: 12-4.5
      Level: III   Tag: None

Explain how rainbows are formed.

When sunlight strikes a water droplet in the air, the light is dispersed into different colors as it passes from the air into the droplet. Some of the light reflects off the back surface of the droplet, by means of total internal reflection. It disperses further when it passes out of the droplet. When the light leaves the droplet, we see the different colors of light as a rainbow.

78)   Item Type: Essay   Objective: None
      Level: None   Tag: None

Explain the principle that allows fiber optic cables to transmit signals.

Fiber optic cables work on the principle of total internal reflection--when a light ray hits a boundary at a critical angle, it is reflected back into the original medium. Light signals within the cable repeatedly bounce off the walls due to total internal reflection. This allows a clear signal to be sent from one end of the cable to the other even though the cable may twist and turn.

1)   Tag Name: ES-6

a)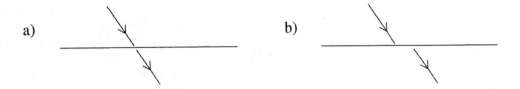

b)

c)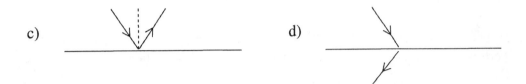

d)

1) Item Type: Multiple Choice   Objective: 13-1.1
Level: I   Tag: None

There is a repulsive force between two charged objects when

a) charges are of unlike sign.   b) they have the same number of protons.

c) charges are of like sign.   d) they have the same number of electrons.

c

2) Item Type: Multiple Choice   Objective: 13-1.1
Level: I   Tag: None

There is an attractive force between two charged objects when

a) charges are of unlike sign.   b) they have the same number of protons.

c) charges are of like sign.   d) they have the same number of electrons.

a

3) Item Type: Multiple Choice   Objective: 13-1.1
Level: I   Tag: None

When a glass rod is rubbed with silk and becomes positively charged,

a) electrons are removed from the rod.   b) protons are added to the silk.

c) protons are removed from the silk.   d) the silk remains neutral.

a

4) Item Type: Multiple Choice   Objective: 13-1.1
Level: I   Tag: None

When there is an equal amount of positive and negative charges on an object, the object is

a) positively charged.   b) negatively charged.

c) neutral.   d) supercharged.

c

5) Item Type: Multiple Choice   Objective: 13-2.2
   Level: I   Tag: None

The electric force between charged objects is

a) attractive only.   b) repulsive only.

c) either attractive or   d) neither attractive nor
repulsive.   repulsive.

c

6) Item Type: Multiple Choice   Objective: 13-1.2
   Level: I   Tag: None

Electric force varies depending on the

a) charge and distance   b) charge and mass of
between charged objects.   charged objects.

c) height and mass of   d) mass and distance
charged objects.   between charged objects.

a

7) Item Type: Multiple Choice   Objective: 13-1.2
   Level: I   Tag: None

Which of the following is *not* true for *both* gravitational and electric forces?

a) The inverse square distance   b) The force depends on a
law applies.   physical property of objects.

c) Potential energy is a   d) The force is either
function of the distance   attractive or repulsive.
between objects.

d

8) Item Type: Multiple Choice   Objective: 13-1.3
   Level: I   Tag: None

Every charged particle produces

a) a negative charge.   b) a positive charge.

c) a magnetic field.   d) an electric field.

d

9) Item Type: Multiple Choice   Objective: 13-1.3
    Level: I   Tag: None

The electric field lines around a negatively charged particle

a) cross positively charged   b) cross negatively charged
particle field lines.   particle field lines.

c) always point inward.   d) always point outward.

c

10) Item Type: Multiple Choice   Objective: 13-1.3
    Level: I   Tag: None

Electric field lines

a) point toward a negative   b) point away from a positive
charge.   charge.

c) never cross one another.   d) all of the above

d

11) Item Type: Multiple Choice   Objective: 13-1.3
    Level: I   Tag: None

Electric field lines indicate

a) direction only.   b) relative strength only.

c) both direction and relative   d) neither direction nor
strength.   strength.

c

12) Item Type: Multiple Choice   Objective: 13-1.3
    Level: I   Tag: None

When compared to a −2 charge, there are

a) an equal number of field   b) twice as many field lines
lines pointing inward toward a   pointing inward toward a +4
+4 charge.   charge.

c) twice as many field lines   d) half as many field lines
pointing outward from a +4   pointing outward from a +4
charge.   charge.

c

13) Item Type: Multiple Choice   Objective: 13-2.1
    Level: I   Tag: None

Potential difference is measured in

a) amperes.   b) volts.

c) coulombs.   d) joules.

b

14) Item Type: Multiple Choice   Objective: 13-2.1
    Level: I   Tag: None

Which of the following is *not* a type of electric cell?

a) electrochemical   b) thermoelectric

c) mechanical   d) photoelectric

c

15) Item Type: Multiple Choice   Objective: 13-2.1
    Level: I   Tag: None

Batteries typically have

a) two positive terminals.   b) two negative terminals.

c) one positive and one   d) no terminals.
negative terminal.

c

16) Item Type: Multiple Choice   Objective: 13-2.2
    Level: I   Tag: None

An electric current is produced when charges are accelerated by an electric field to move to a position of potential energy that is

a) higher.   b) lower.

c) equal.   d) infinite.

b

17) Item Type: Multiple Choice   Objective: 13-2.2
    Level: I   Tag: None

Current is the rate at which charges move through a(n)

        a) conductor.   b) insulator.

        c) voltage.   d) joule.

a

18) Item Type: Multiple Choice   Objective: 13-2.2
    Level: I   Tag: None

Potential differences cause

a) electrons to move from the positive terminal to the negative terminal.

b) electrons to move from the negative terminal to the positive terminal.

c) protons to move from the positive terminal to the negative terminal.

d) protons to move from the negative terminal to the positive terminal.

b

19) Item Type: Multiple Choice   Objective: 13-2.3
    Level: I   Tag: None

The brightness of a light bulb is determined by its filament's

        a) voltage.   b) amperes.

        c) watts.   d) resistance.

d

20) Item Type: Multiple Choice   Objective: 13-2.3
    Level: I   Tag: None

Resistance is caused by

        a) internal friction.   b) electron charge.

        c) proton charge.   d) a heat source.

a

Chapter 13

21) Item Type: Multiple Choice   Objective: 13-2.3
    Level: I   Tag: None

The SI unit of resistance is the

    a) volt.   b) ampere.

    c) ohm.   d) joule.

c

22) Item Type: Multiple Choice   Objective: 13-2.3
    Level: I   Tag: None

Whether or not charges will move in a material depends partly on how tightly _____ are held in the atoms of the material.

    a) electrons   b) neutrons

    c) protons   d) resistors

a

23) Item Type: Multiple Choice   Objective: 13-2.3
    Level: I   Tag: None

Which of the following does *not* affect a material's resistance?

    a) length   b) temperature

    c) the type of material   d) Ohm's law

d

24) Item Type: Multiple Choice   Objective: 13-2.4
    Level: II   Tag: None

A flashlight bulb with a potential difference of 4.5 V across its filament has a power output of 8.0 W. How much current is in the bulb filament?

    a) 3.7 A   b) 1.8 A

    c) 0.23 A   d) 0.56 A

b

25) Item Type: Multiple Choice   Objective: 13-2.4
Level: II   Tag: None

What is the potential difference across a resistor that dissipates 5.00 W of power and has a current of 5.0 A?

a) 1.0 V   b) 125 V

c) 4.00 V   d) 0.20 V

a

26) Item Type: Multiple Choice   Objective: 13-2.4
Level: II   Tag: None

There is a potential difference of 12 V across a resistor with 0.25 A of current in it. The resistance of the resistor is

a) 48 Ω   b) 24 Ω

c) 12 Ω   d) .021 Ω

a

27) Item Type: Multiple Choice   Objective: 13-2.4
Level: II   Tag: None

A 13 Ω resistor has 0.050 A of current in it. What is the potential difference across the resistor?

a) 6.5 V   b) 0.65 V

c) 0.065 V   d) 0.0065 V

b

28) Item Type: Multiple Choice   Objective: 13-2.4
Level: II   Tag: None

A resistor has a resistance of 280 Ω. How much current is in the resistor if there is a potential difference of 120 V across the resistor?

a) 160 A   b) 0.43 A

c) 0.12 A   d) 2.3 A

b

Chapter 13

29) Item Type: Multiple Choice   Objective: 13-2.4
     Level: II   Tag: None

A set of electric trains are powered by a 9V battery. What is the resistance of the trains if they draw 3.0 A of current?

a) 3 Ω   b) 0.03 Ω

c) 27 Ω   d) 2.7 Ω

a

30) Item Type: Multiple Choice   Objective: 13-2.5
     Level: I   Tag: None

The resistance of an insulator is

a) absent.   b) very low.

c) moderate.   d) high.

d

31) Item Type: Multiple Choice   Objective: 13-2.5
     Level: I   Tag: None

What happens to the resistance of a superconductor when its temperature drops below the critical temperature?

a) Resistance increases.   b) Resistance doubles.

c) Resistance drops to zero.   d) Resistance is reduced by
                                  one-half.

c

32) Item Type: Multiple Choice   Objective: 13-2.5
     Level: I   Tag: None

Which of the following shows how conductors, insulators, superconductors, and semiconductors rank in order of least resistance to most resistance?

a) superconductors,   b) semiconductors,
conductors, semiconductors,   superconductors, conductors,
insulators   insulators

c) insulators, conductors,   d) none of the above
semiconductors,
superconductors

a

Chapter 13

33) Item Type: Multiple Choice   Objective: 13-3.2
Level: I   Tag: None

Appliances connected so that they form a single pathway for charges to flow are connected in a(n)

a) series circuit.   b) parallel circuit.

c) open circuit.   d) closed circuit.

a

34) Item Type: Multiple Choice   Objective: 13-3.3
Level: II   Tag: None

If a lamp is measured to have a resistance of 45 Ω when it operates at a power of 80.0 W, what is the current in the lamp?

a) 2.10 A   b) 1.3 A

c) 0.91 A   d) 0.83 A

b

35) Item Type: Multiple Choice   Objective: 13-3.3
Level: II   Tag: None

An electric toaster has a power rating of 1100 W at 110 V. What is the resistance of the heating coil?

a) 7.5 Ω b) 9.0 Ω

c) 10 Ω d) 11 Ω

d

36) Item Type: Multiple Choice   Objective: 13-3.3
Level: II   Tag: None

If a lamp is measured to have a resistance of 120 Ω when it operates at a power of 1.00×10^2 W, what is the potential difference across the lamp?

a) 110 V   b) 120 V

c) 0.913 V   d) 220 V

a

37) Item Type: Multiple Choice   Objective: 13-3.3
Level: II   Tag: None

If a 325 W heater has a current of 6.00 A, what is the resistance of the heating element?

a) 88.1 Ω   b) 54.2 Ω

c) 9.03 Ω   d) 11.4 Ω

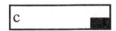

38) Item Type: Multiple Choice   Objective: 13-3.3
Level: II   Tag: None

A color television draws about 2.5 A when it is connected to a 120 V outlet. Assuming electrical energy costs $0.060 per kW•h, what is the cost of running the television for exactly 8 hours?

a) $1.44   b) $0.03

c) $0.14   d) $0.30

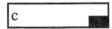

39) Item Type: Multiple Choice   Objective: 13-3.3
Level: II   Tag: None

A microwave draws 5.0 A when it is connected to a 120 V outlet. If electrical energy cost $0.090/kW•h, what is the cost of running the microwave for exactly 6 hours?

a) $2.70   b) $1.60

c) $0.72   d) $0.32

40) Item Type: Multiple Choice   Objective: 13-3.4
Level: I   Tag: None

What happens to the overall resistance of a circuit when too many appliances are connected across a 120 V outlet?

a) Resistance is increased.   b) Resistance remains the same.

c) Resistance is decreased.   d) Resistance is zero.

41) Item Type: Multiple Choice   Objective: 13-3.4
     Level: I   Tag: None

A device that protects a circuit from current overload is called a(n)

        a) resistor.   b) capacitor.

        c) circuit breaker.   d) closed circuit.

c

42) Item Type: Short Answer   Objective: 13-1.1
     Level: I   Tag: None

When does an atom have a net charge?

Whenever there is an imbalance in the number of protons and electrons in an atom, it has a net charge.

43) Item Type: Short Answer   Objective: 13-1.1
     Level: I   Tag: None

What is charging by friction?

When two materials are rubbed together, electrons can be transferred from one material to the other. The material that gets the electrons becomes negatively charged and the material that loses the electrons becomes positively charged.

44) Item Type: Short Answer   Objective: 13-1.1
     Level: I   Tag: None

What is charging by contact?

When a negatively charged object touches a neutral object, electrons can flow into the neutral object, making it negatively charged. When a positively charged object touches a neutral object, electrons can flow into the positively charged object, causing the neutral object to become positively charged.

45) Item Type: Short Answer   Objective: 13-1.2
     Level: II   Tag: None

How does the electric force between two charged objects depend on distance?

The electric force between two objects is inversely proportional to the square of the distance between the objects. This means if the distance doubles, the force decreases by a factor of 4.

46) Item Type: Short Answer   Objective: 13-1.2
     Level: II   Tag: Fig. 17-18

In the figure shown above, why do only half of the lines originating from the positive charge terminate on the negative charge?

Because the positive charge is twice as great as the negative charge.

47) Item Type: Short Answer   Objective: 13-1.2
     Level: I   Tag: Fig. 17-15ao

Is the charge shown in the figure above positive or negative?

| positive |

48) Item Type: Short Answer   Objective: 13-1.2
     Level: I   Tag: 17-15a1

Is the charge shown in the figure above positive or negative?

| negative |

49) Item Type: Short Answer   Objective: 13-1.3
     Level: I   Tag: None

What is electrical potential energy?

| potential energy associated with a charged object due to its position in an electric field |

50) Item Type: Short Answer   Objective: 13-2.2
     Level: II   Tag: None

Why is the direction of current in a wire opposite to the direction the electrons move in a wire?

| A negative charge moving in one direction has the same effect as a positive charge moving in the opposite direction. By convention, the direction of current is defined in terms of positive charge movement. |

51) Item Type: Short Answer   Objective: 13-2.1
     Level: II   Tag: None

What determines the electrical potential energy of a charge?

| The electrical potential energy of a charge is determined by the position of the charge relative to the position of all other electrical charges. |

52) Item Type: Short Answer   Objective: 13-2.1
     Level: I   Tag: None

How are electrical potential energy and potential difference related?

| Potential difference is the change in the electrical potential energy of a charged particle divided by its charge. |

Chapter 13

53) Item Type: Short Answer
Level: I

Objective: 13-2.2
Tag: None

What is electric current?

It is the rate at which electric charges move through a conductor.

54) Item Type: Short Answer
Level: I

Objective: 13-2.3
Tag: None

Why do electrical devices feel warm after they have been on for a period of time?

Electrical devices feel warm because kinetic energy is transferred from moving electrons to surrounding materials, causing the atoms to vibrate.

55) Item Type: Short Answer
Level: II

Objective: 13-2.4
Tag: None

There is a potential difference of 13 V across a resistor with 1.4 A of current in it. What is the resistance of the resistor?

9.3 Ω

56) Item Type: Short Answer
Level: II

Objective: 13-2.4
Tag: None

A 180 Ω resistor has 0.10 A of current in it. What is the potential difference across the resistor?

18 V

57) Item Type: Short Answer
Level: II

Objective: 13-2.4
Tag: None

A resistor has a resistance of 1.8 Ω. How much current is in the resistor if there is a potential difference of 3.0 V across the resistor?

1.7 A

58) Item Type: Short Answer
Level: I

Objective: 13-2.4
Tag: None

What is resistance in a conductor?

Resistance is internal friction that slows the movement of electrons in a conductor.

59) Item Type: Short Answer   Objective: 13-2.5
    Level: 1   Tag: None

What is the difference between a conductor and an insulator?

A conductor has a low resistance because electrons can flow easily under the influence of an electric field. An insulator has a high resistance because the charges inside the insulator do not move easily.

60) Item Type: Short Answer   Objective: 13-3.1
    Level: 1   Tag: resistor #2

Identify the types of elements in the schematic diagram above and the number of each type.

two resistors, one battery, one switch

61) Item Type: Short Answer   Objective: 13-3.1
    Level: 1   Tag: resistor #3

Identify the types of elements in the schematic diagram above and the number of each type.

three resistors, one battery, and one light bulb

62) Item Type: Short Answer   Objective: 13-3.1
    Level: 1   Tag: None

Draw a schematic diagram that contains three identical resistors and one battery in a series circuit.

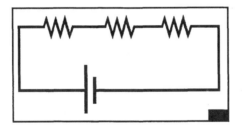

63) Item Type: Short Answer   Objective: 13-3.1
    Level: 1   Tag: circuit #1

Is a current flowing in the schematic diagram above? Explain your answer.

No, because the switch is open, so there is not a closed-loop path for the electrons to follow.

64) Item Type: Short Answer   Objective: 13-3.1
    Level: 1   Tag: diagram #1

Which bulb(s) will have a current in the schematic diagram above?

Only the first light bulb will light. The other two bulbs are beyond the open switch and, therefore, will not receive current.

65) Item Type: Short Answer   Objective: 13-3.2
Level: I   Tag: resistor #6

Does the schematic diagram above represent a series or parallel circuit?

parallel circuit

66) Item Type: Short Answer   Objective: 13-3.2
Level: I   Tag: answer spec #1

Does the schematic diagram above represent a series or parallel circuit?

series circuit

67) Item Type: Short Answer   Objective: 13-3.3
Level: I   Tag: None

What is electric power?

the rate at which electrical work is done

68) Item Type: Short Answer   Objective: 13-3.3
Level: II   Tag: None

A hair dryer draws 11 A when it is connected to 120 V. If electrical energy costs $0.09/kW•h, what is the cost of using the hair dryer for exactly 15 minutes?

$0.03

69) Item Type: Short Answer   Objective: 13-3.3
Level: II   Tag: None

If a 75 W light bulb operates at a voltage of 120 V, what is the current in the bulb?

0.62 A

70) Item Type: Short Answer   Objective: 13-3.4
Level: I   Tag: None

What effect does decreased resistance have on a circuit?

Decreased resistance increases the current in the circuit.

71) Item Type: Short Answer   Objective: 13-3.4
Level: I   Tag: None

What is a short circuit?

A short circuit is an alternate pathway for current created by contact between two wires normally isolated from each other by insulation.

72) Item Type: Short Answer   Objective: 13-3.4
     Level: I   Tag: None

What does a circuit breaker do?

A circuit breaker responds to current overload by opening a circuit.

73) Item Type: Essay   Objective: 13-2.2
     Level: II   Tag: None

How does a battery set charges in a circuit in motion?

In the presence of an electric field, charges are accelerated to move to a position of lower potential energy. There is a potential difference, or voltage, across the terminals of a battery. Electrons in the circuit move away from the negative terminal and toward the positive terminal due to the electric field produced in the circuit by the battery.

74) Item Type: Essay   Objective: 13-2.3
     Level: II   Tag: None

What are some factors that would cause the resistance of two wires to be different? Which factors would cause the resistance to increase and which factors would cause the resistance to decrease?

Two wires can have different resistances because of length, cross-sectional area, temperature, and the kind of material the wire is made of. The longer a wire is the greater the resistance, and the greater the cross-sectional area the less the resistance.

75) Item Type: Essay   Objective: 13-3.2
     Level: II   Tag: None

Compare and contrast series and parallel circuits.

Both series and parallel circuits provide conducting paths for electricity. However, a series circuit provides a single pathway. An interruption affects the movement of electrons throughout the entire circuit. Parallel circuits provide two or more conducting pathways. An interruption does not necessarily affect the entire circuit, as alternate paths are available for electron movement to continue.

76) Item Type: Thinking Critically   Objective: 13-1.1
     Level: III   Tag: None

You can pick up static electricity by walking on a wool rug in leather-soled shoes. Explain why you are then negatively charged and what happens when you grab for a metal object such as a doorknob.

You have been negatively charged by friction because you have picked up electrons from the rug. As you reach for a metal object, electrons will move from your body to the object because of their difference in electrical potential energy, and you will experience a mild shock.

77) Item Type: Thinking Critically   Objective: 13-3.2
     Level: III   Tag: None

Does the wiring in your house use series or parallel circuits? Explain.

> Parallel circuits; otherwise everything would have to be on for anything to be on. There may be series circuits within the system, however. For example, lights that can be operated from switches at either entrance to a room or wall sockets that work only when a switch is in the on position use series circuits.

1)   Tag Name: Fig. 17-18

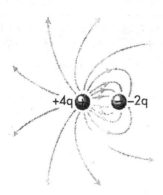

2)   Tag Name: Fig. 17-15ao

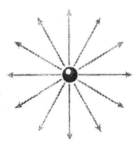

3)   Tag Name: resistor #3

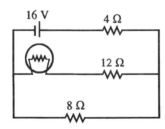

4)   Tag Name: circuit #1

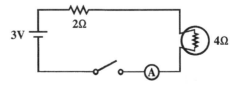

5)   Tag Name: diagram #1

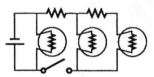

6)   Tag Name: resistor #6

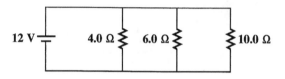

7)   Tag Name: answer spec #1

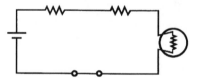

8)   Tag Name: 17-15a1

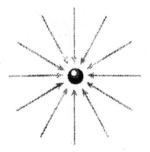

9)   Tag Name: resistor #2

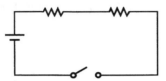

1) Item Type: Multiple Choice   Objective: 14-1.1
   Level: I   Tag: None

An example of a naturally occurring magnetic rock is

        a) lodestone.   b) soapstone.

        c) limestone.   d) peastone.

a

2) Item Type: Multiple Choice   Objective: 14-1.1
   Level: I   Tag: None

Magnetically soft substances

        a) retain their magnetism   b) lose their magnetism more
        longer than others.   easily than others.

        c) cannot be magnetized easily.   d) pick up more iron nails than
                                    magnetically hard substances.

b

3) Item Type: Multiple Choice   Objective: 14-1.1
   Level: I   Tag: None

The north pole of one magnet will be

        a) attracted to the north pole   b) attracted to the south pole
        of another magnet.   of the same magnet.

        c) repelled by the north pole   d) repelled by the south pole
        of another magnet.   of another magnet.

c

4) Item Type: Multiple Choice   Objective: 14-1.1
   Level: I   Tag: None

Like magnet poles always

        a) repel each other.   b) attract each other.

        c) cancel out each other's   d) point toward the north pole.
        magnetic fields.

a

Chapter 14

5) Item Type: Multiple Choice   Objective: 14-1.2
Level: I   Tag: None

The magnetism of a piece of magnetized iron can be weakened by

a) heating the iron and hammering it.

b) putting it near a piece of unmagnetized iron.

c) bending the iron.

d) none of the above

a

6) Item Type: Multiple Choice   Objective: 14-1.2
Level: I   Tag: None

Magnetic force

a) is strongest near a magnet's poles.

b) is a field force.

c) acts at a distance.

d) all of the above

d

7) Item Type: Multiple Choice   Objective: 14-1.2
Level: II   Tag: Compass needle

Which of the compass needle orientations in the figure above might correctly describe the magnet's field at that point?

a) a

b) b

c) c

d) d

a

8) Item Type: Multiple Choice   Objective: 14-1.2
Level: I   Tag: None

The strength of the magnetic field

a) decreases as distance from the magnet decreases.

b) decreases as distance from the magnet increases.

c) increases as distance from the magnet increases.

d) remains the same at any distance from a magnet.

b

9) Item Type: Multiple Choice   Objective: 14-1.2
   Level: I   Tag: None

Magnetic fields exist

    a) near a magnet.   b) farther away from a magnet.

    c) within a magnet.   d) all of the above

d

10) Item Type: Multiple Choice   Objective: 14-1.3
    Level: I   Tag: None

What material was used to make the first compass?

    a) lodestone   b) limestone

    c) iron   d) steel

a

11) Item Type: Multiple Choice   Objective: 14-1.3
    Level: I   Tag: None

What instrument is used to trace the direction of a magnetic field?

    a) lodestone   b) limestone

    c) compass   d) needle

c

12) Item Type: Multiple Choice   Objective: 14-1.3
    Level: I   Tag: None

A compass needle naturally points toward

    a) the geographic North Pole.   b) the S pole of a magnet

    c) Earth's North Magnetic   d) all of the above
    Pole.

d

13) Item Type: Multiple Choice   Objective: 14-1.3
    Level: I   Tag: None

What causes a compass needle to point to geographic north?

    a) The pole of the compass is attracted to Earth's Geographic North Pole.

    b) The compass needle aligns with Earth's magnetic field.

    c) The force of Earth's rotation causes the needle of the compass to seek the north pole.

    d) all of the above

b

14) Item Type: Multiple Choice   Objective: 14-1.4
    Level: I   Tag: None

Earth's magnetic poles are located in

    a) Canada and Australia.

    b) Canada and Alaska.

    c) Canada and Antarctica.

    d) the same positions as the geographic poles.

c

15) Item Type: Multiple Choice   Objective: 14-2.1
    Level: I   Tag: None

Magnetic fields are produced by

    a) magnetic force.

    b) electric currents.

    c) gravitational force.

    d) water currents.

b

16) Item Type: Multiple Choice   Objective: 14-2.1
    Level: I   Tag: None

A magnetic field around a current-carrying wire forms

    a) lines tangent to the wire.

    b) lines perpendicular to the wire.

    c) lines parallel to the wire.

    d) concentric circles around the wire.

d

17) Item Type: Multiple Choice   Objective: 14-2.2
    Level: I   Tag: None

The strength of a magnetic field created by current in a wire can be safely increased by

a) increasing the current in the wire.

b) decreasing the current in the wire.

c) using longer wire.

d) wrapping the wire into a coil.

d

18) Item Type: Multiple Choice   Objective: 14-2.2
    Level: I   Tag: None

The strength of the magnetic field of a solenoid can be increased by

a) decreasing the number of loops on the solenoid.

b) decreasing the current in the solenoid.

c) increasing the number of loops on the solenoid.

d) increasing the resistance of the solenoid.

c

19) Item Type: Multiple Choice   Objective: 14-2.2
    Level: I   Tag: None

The strength of the magnetic field of a solenoid can be increased by

a) decreasing the number of loops on the solenoid.

b) decreasing the current in the solenoid.

c) inserting an iron rod through the center of the solenoid.

d) inserting a rubber rod through the center of the solenoid.

c

20) Item Type: Multiple Choice   Objective: 14-2.3
    Level: I   Tag: None

In a magnetized substance, the domains

a) are randomly distributed.

b) line up more uniformly in one direction.

c) cancel each other.

d) can never be reoriented.

b

21) Item Type: Multiple Choice   Objective: 14-2.3
    Level: I   Tag: None

Which orientation characterizes the magnetic domains in an unmagnetized piece of iron?

   a) parallel to the magnetic axis   b) antiparallel to the magnetic axis

   c) random   d) perpendicular to the magnetic axis

c

22) Item Type: Multiple Choice   Objective: 14-2.3
    Level: I   Tag: None

When an iron rod is inserted into a solenoid's center, the magnetic field produced by the current in the loops

   a) causes the iron to return to   b) forces the domains in the
   an unmagnetized state.   iron out of alignment.

   c) causes a random orientation   d) causes alignment of the
   of the domains in the iron.   domains in the iron.

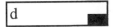

d

23) Item Type: Multiple Choice   Objective: 14-2.2
    Level: I   Tag: None

A potential difference causes

   a) electrons to move from the   b) electrons to move from the
   positive terminal to the   negative terminal to the
   negative terminal of a battery.   positive terminal of a battery.

   c) protons to move from the   d) protons to move from the
   positive terminal to the   negative terminal to the positive
   negative terminal of a battery.   terminal of a battery.

b

24) Item Type: Multiple Choice   Objective: 14-2.4
    Level: I   Tag: None

Which of the following contains a commutator?

   a) galvanometer   b) transformer

   c) electric motor   d) electromagnet

c

25) Item Type: Multiple Choice   Objective: 14-2.4
     Level: I   Tag: None

A device that converts electric energy into mechanical energy is a(n)

         a) generator.   b) electric motor.

         c) commutator.   d) transformer.

b

26) Item Type: Multiple Choice   Objective: 14-2.4
     Level: I   Tag: None

An electric motor and a generator are similar in that both

         a) use electricity.   b) produce mechanical energy.

         c) transform energy into a   d) create energy.
         different form.

c

27) Item Type: Multiple Choice   Objective: 14-3.1
     Level: I   Tag: None

Pushing a magnet through an electric field requires work. The greater the electric field,

         a) the stronger the force   b) the less the force required
         required to push the magnet   to push the magnet through
         through the electric field.   the electric field.

         c) The less will be the   d) the more the loop will
         electromagnetic induction.   rotate.

a

28) Item Type: Multiple Choice   Objective: 14-3.1
     Level: I   Tag: None

When a charge moves along or opposite the direction of the magnetic field lines, the magnetic force is

         a) zero.   b) a maximum.

         c) equal to the magnetic force   d) none of the above
         when it moves perpendicular
         to the magnetic field lines.

a

Chapter 14

29) Item Type: Multiple Choice   Objective: 14-3.1
    Level: I   Tag: None

When a wire is moving perpendicular to a magnetic field, the force on the charges is

a) at a minimum.   b) at a maximum.

c) zero.   d) all of the above

b

30) Item Type: Multiple Choice   Objective: 14-3.2
    Level: I   Tag: None

Generators convert

a) mechanical energy to   b) electrical energy to
electrical energy.   mechanical energy.

c) chemical energy to electrical d) electrical energy to chemical
energy.   energy.

a

31) Item Type: Multiple Choice   Objective: 14-3.2
    Level: I   Tag: None

In an AC generator, the magnitude of the current produced

a) depends on the orientation   b) is a minimum when the
of the loop in a magnetic   loop is perpendicular to the
field.   magnetic field.

c) varies with time.   d) all of the above

d

32) Item Type: Multiple Choice   Objective: 14-3.2
    Level: I   Tag: None

In an AC generator, when charges experience the maximum magnetic force,

a) the current is small.   b) the current is large.

c) the current is zero.   d) the current increases.

d

33) Item Type: Multiple Choice   Objective: 14-3.2
     Level: I   Tag: None

When a wire is moving parallel to a magnetic field,

a) no current is induced in the wire.

b) maximum current is induced in the wire.

c) the same current is induced as if it were perpendicular to the field.

d) an alternating current is induced.

a

34) Item Type: Multiple Choice   Objective: 14-3.2
     Level: I   Tag: None

Light travels as

a) electrical waves.

b) magnetic waves.

c) electromagnetic waves.

d) electrochemical waves.

c

35) Item Type: Multiple Choice   Objective: 14-3.2
     Level: I   Tag: None

Both electric and magnetic fields in an electromagnetic wave are

a) perpendicular to the direction that the wave travels.

b) parallel to the direction that the wave travels.

c) opposite the direction that the wave travels.

d) tangential to the direction that the wave travels.

a

36) Item Type: Multiple Choice   Objective: 14-3.3
     Level: I   Tag: None

Transformers can

a) increase voltage.

b) decrease voltage.

c) neither increase nor decrease voltage.

d) increase or decrease voltage.

d

230

37) Item Type: Multiple Choice   Objective: 14-3.3
    Level: I   Tag: None

A transformer changes

        a) both the amperage and the   b) the voltage of an electric
        voltage of an electric current.   current.

        c) the amperage of an electric   d) the type of an electric
        current.   current.

b

38) Item Type: Short Answer   Objective: 14-1.1
    Level: I   Tag: None

What is a magnetic pole?

A magnetic pole is an area of a magnet where the magnetic force appears to be the
strongest.

39) Item Type: Short Answer   Objective: 14-1.1
    Level: I   Tag: magnet attraction #3

Will the magnets in the figure above attract or repel each other?

The magnets will attract each other.

40) Item Type: Short Answer   Objective: 14-1.1
    Level: I   Tag: magnet attraction #1

Will the magnets in the figure above attract or repel each other?

The magnets will repel each other.

41) Item Type: Short Answer   Objective: 14-1.1
    Level: I   Tag: magnet attraction #4

Will the magnets in the figure above attract or repel each other?

The magnets will attract each other.

42) Item Type: Short Answer   Objective: 14-1.1
    Level: I   Tag: magnet attraction #2

Will the magnets in the figure above attract or repel each other?

The magnets will repel each other.

43) Item Type: Short Answer   Objective: 14-1.2
     Level: I   Tag: None

How can the magnetic field around a permanent magnet be determined?

It can be determined with a compass. The direction of the magnetic field is defined as the direction in which the north pole of a compass needle points at that location.

44) Item Type: Short Answer   Objective: 14-1.2
     Level: II   Tag: None

A bar magnet is suspended and allowed to rotate freely. If the magnetic field of Earth is considered to be equivalent to that of a large bar magnet, which pole of the suspended magnet would point toward the Geographic North Pole of Earth?

The north (N) pole would point to the Geographic North Pole of Earth.

45) Item Type: Short Answer   Objective: 14-1.2
     Level: I   Tag: None

What do magnetic field lines that are close together indicate?

Magnetic field lines that are close together indicate a strong magnetic field.

46) Item Type: Short Answer   Objective: 14-1.2
     Level: I   Tag: None

What determines the strength of the magnetic field?

The strength of the magnetic field depends on the material from which the magnet is made and the degree to which it is magnetized.

47) Item Type: Short Answer   Objective: 14-1.3
     Level: I   Tag: None

How does a compass indicate direction?

A compass aligns with Earth's magnetic field just as iron filings align with the field of a bar magnet. The N pole of the compass points toward Earth's Geographic North Pole.

48) Item Type: Short Answer   Objective: 14-1.4
     Level: I   Tag: None

Where is Earth's magnetic N pole located?

Antarctica

49) Item Type: Short Answer   Objective: 14-1.4
     Level: I   Tag: None

Where is Earth's magnetic S pole located?

Northeastern Canada

50) Item Type: Short Answer   Objective: 14-2.2
    Level: I   Tag: None

What is a solenoid?

A solenoid is a long, wound coil of insulated wire.

51) Item Type: Short Answer   Objective: 14-2.2
    Level: I   Tag: None

How does inserting an iron rod through the center of a solenoid increase the strength of its magnetic field?

The magnetic field of the rod adds to the coil's field, creating a stronger magnet than the solenoid alone.

52) Item Type: Short Answer   Objective: 14-2.2
    Level: II   Tag: None

A current-carrying wire is perpendicular to the surface of a table. The direction of current is toward the floor. What is the direction of the magnetic field as viewed from above?

clockwise

53) Item Type: Short Answer   Objective: 14-2.2
    Level: II   Tag: None

A solenoid is standing on its end on a table. The direction of current is counterclockwise. Which end of the solenoid is an N pole?

the top

54) Item Type: Short Answer   Objective: 14-2.2
    Level: II   Tag: None

In order to maximize the strength of an electromagnet, the current should be in what position relative to the magnetic field?

perpendicular

55) Item Type: Short Answer   Objective: 14-2.2
    Level: II   Tag: None

What is the relationship between the electric field and the magnetic field in an electromagnetic wave?

The electric and magnetic fields are perpendicular to each other and to the direction the EM wave travels. As the wave moves along, the changing electric and magnetic fields regenerate each other.

56) Item Type: Short Answer   Objective: 14-2.3
    Level: 1   Tag: None

What causes the magnetic properties of bar magnets?

In the material that a bar magnet is composed of, the magnetic fields of the electrons do not all cancel, so each atom has its own magnetic field. The domains in the bar magnet are aligned more in a common direction.

57) Item Type: Short Answer   Objective: 14-2.3
    Level: 1   Tag: None

Describe the orientation of the domains inside an unmagnetized piece of iron.

The domains are randomly oriented in an unmagnetized piece of iron.

58) Item Type: Short Answer   Objective: 14-2.4
    Level: 1   Tag: None

What is a galvanometer?

A galvanometer is an instrument that measures the amount of current in a circuit.

59) Item Type: Short Answer   Objective: 14-2.4
    Level: 1   Tag: None

What is the relationship between the current in an electromagnet and its magnetic field?

The greater the current, the stronger its magnetic field.

60) Item Type: Short Answer   Objective: 14-2.4
    Level: 1   Tag: None

What do galvanometers use to measure the current in a circuit?

Galvanometers measure the current in a circuit using the magnetic field produced by the current in a coil.

61) Item Type: Short Answer   Objective: 14-3.1
    Level: 1   Tag: None

What is electromagnetic induction?

Electromagnetic induction is the production of a current in a conducting circuit by a change in the strength, position, or orientation of an external magnetic field.

62) Item Type: Short Answer   Objective: 14-3.1
    Level: 1   Tag: None

What is Faraday's law?

An electric current can be produced in a circuit by a changing magnetic field.

63) Item Type: Short Answer   Objective: 14-3.1
       Level: 1   Tag: None

What is the relationship between the strength of a magnetic field and the force required to push a magnet through the field?

The greater the magnetic field, the stronger the force required to push the magnet through the field.

64) Item Type: Short Answer   Objective: 14-3.2
       Level: 1   Tag: None

Which type of current, alternating or direct, is used by most households and businesses?

alternating current

65) Item Type: Short Answer   Objective: 14-3.2
       Level: 1   Tag: None

What is a generator?

A generator is a device that uses electromagnetic induction to convert mechanical energy to electrical energy.

66) Item Type: Short Answer   Objective: 14-3.2
       Level: 1   Tag: None

How are generators different from electric motors?

Generators convert mechanical energy to electrical energy, whereas electric motors convert electric energy to mechanical energy.

67) Item Type: Short Answer   Objective: 14-3.2
       Level: 1   Tag: None

Explain how power dams work.

Dams harness the kinetic energy of falling water by forcing water at the top of the dam through small channels. As the water falls through the channels it turns the blades of turbine fans that are attached to an electric circuit that rotates within a magnetic field.

68) Item Type: Short Answer   Objective: 14-3.2
       Level: 1   Tag: None

What is the most common source of mechanical energy used in commercial power plants?

running water

Chapter 14

69) Item Type: Short Answer   Objective: 14-3.2
    Level: 1   Tag: None

In addition to running water, what are other sources of mechanical energy used by generators to generate electrical energy?

nuclear burning coal, fission, wind, hot water from geysers (geothermal), and solar power

70) Item Type: Short Answer   Objective: 14-3.3
    Level: 1   Tag: None

How are electric and magnetic field waves oriented relative to each other in an electromagnetic wave?

Electric and magnetic field waves are oriented at 90 degree angles relative to each other.

71) Item Type: Short Answer   Objective: 14-3.3
    Level: 1   Tag: None

What is a transformer?

A transformer is a device that can change one alternating current voltage to a different alternating current voltage.

72) Item Type: Short Answer   Objective: 14-3.3
    Level: 1   Tag: None

What are step-up and step-down transformers used for?

Step-up and step-down transformers are used in the transmission of electrical energy from power plants to homes and businesses. Step-up transformers are used near power plants to increase the voltage of the current to about 120 000 V, to minimize energy loss in transmission. Step-down transformers near homes and businesses are used to decrease the voltage of the current for safer use in appliances.

73) Item Type: Short Answer   Objective: 14-3.3
    Level: 1   Tag: None

What does a step-down transformer on a power line near your home do?

The step-down transformer reduces the voltage of the current to about 120 V. Most household appliances in the United States operate at 120 V.

74) Item Type: Short Answer   Objective: 14-3.3
    Level: 1   Tag: None

What is the relationship between voltage across the secondary coil of a transformer and the number of loops it has?

The voltage across the secondary coil of a transformer is proportional to the number of loops it has.

75) Item Type: Short Answer   Objective: 14-1.1
    Level: II   Tag: None

If the head of an iron nail touches a magnet, the nail will be magnetized. If the nail touches the north pole of the magnet, what kind of pole is at the point of the nail? Explain.

> The head of the magnetized nail, which is touching the north pole of the magnet, will be a south pole. Otherwise, it would be repelled by the magnet. The tip of the nail will be a north pole.

76) Item Type: Essay   Objective: 14-1.3
    Level: II   Tag: None

Is the source of Earth's magnetism its iron core? What are other theories of the source of Earth's magnetism?

> No. The very high temperatures of Earth's core would not allow iron in the core to retain any magnetic properties. Instead, some scientists theorize that Earth's magnetism is the result of the circulation of ions or electrons in the liquid layer of Earth's core.

77) Item Type: Essay   Objective: 14-1.4
    Level: II   Tag: None

Compare and contrast Earth's magnetic poles with its geographic poles.

> Earth's magnetic poles are not in the same positions as the geographic poles. Also, Earth's magnetic field points from the geographic South Pole to the geographic North Pole. The magnetic pole in Antarctica is actually a magnetic N pole and the magnetic pole in northern Canada is actually a magnetic S pole.

78) Item Type: Essay   Objective: 14-2.2
    Level: II   Tag: None

Describe how to find the direction of the magnetic field produced by a current.

> Imagine grasping an insulated wire with the right hand so that the thumb points in the direction of the positive current. When the hand holds the wire, the fingers encircle the wire with the fingertips pointing in the direction of the magnetic field.

79) Item Type: Essay   Objective: 14-3.2
    Level: II   Tag: None

How is running water converted from mechanical energy to electrical energy?

> Water is forced through small channels at the top of a dam. As the water falls to the base of the dam, it turns the blades of large turbine fans. The fans are attached to a core wrapped with many loops of wire that rotate within a strong magnetic field. A current is induced in the wire through electromagnetic induction.

80) Item Type: Essay   Objective: 14-1.2
     Level: III   Tag: None

Holding a strong magnet next to a videotape or an audiotape usually destroys all the information on that tape. Use your knowledge of magnetism to explain why.

Video and audiotapes systems encode information by aligning magnetic crystals. A strong magnetic field would cause the magnetic crystals to reorient themselves thereby destroying the original information.

Chapter 14

1) Tag Name: magnet attraction #1

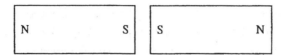

2) Tag Name: magnet attraction #2

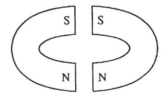

3) Tag Name: magnet attraction #3

4) Tag Name: magnet attraction #4

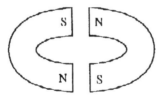

5) Tag Name: Compass needle

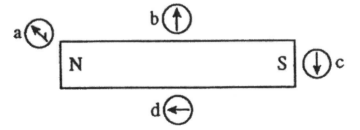

1) Item Type: Multiple Choice   Objective: 15-1.1
   Level: I   Tag: None

   A signal is a sign that represents

       a) information.   b) questions.

       c) symbols.   d) dots and dashes.

   a

2) Item Type: Multiple Choice   Objective: 15-1.1
   Level: I   Tag: None

   A code is

       a) a special kind of signal.   b) the meaning of a signal.

       c) a change in a signal.   d) unrelated to signals.

   b

3) Item Type: Multiple Choice   Objective: 15-1.1
   Level: I   Tag: None

   Language is an example of a

       a) signal.   b) script.

       c) symbol.   d) code.

   d

4) Item Type: Multiple Choice   Objective: 15-1.1
   Level: I   Tag: None

   To send sound using electricity, the first step is to

       a) send the electrical signal along a wire.   b) convert the electrical signal into sound.

       c) convert the sound into electric current.   d) broadcast the sound through an amplifier.

   c

5) Item Type: Multiple Choice   Objective: 15-1.2
   Level: I   Tag: None

   Which of the following is *not* a means of telecommunication?

       a) telephone   b) postal delivery

       c) e-mail   d) telegraph

   b

6) Item Type: Multiple Choice   Objective: 15-1.3
Level: I   Tag: None

An analog signal

a) never varies.

b) varies continuously within a range.

c) only shows a single reading.

d) uses a single flashing light.

b

7) Item Type: Multiple Choice   Objective: 15-1.3
Level: I   Tag: None

The binary number system is associated with

a) analog signals.

b) digital signals.

c) radio signals.

d) telephone signals.

b

8) Item Type: Multiple Choice   Objective: 15-1.3
Level: I   Tag: None

Morse code was developed for

a) sending ship-to-ship communications.

b) sending ship-to-shore communications.

c) sending information by telegraph.

d) sending information by telephone.

c

9) Item Type: Multiple Choice   Objective: 15-1.3
Level: I   Tag: None

A digital signal is

a) a signal that can be interpreted as a sequence of digits.

b) based on the binary number system.

c) composed of discrete fixed values.

d) all of the above.

d

10) Item Type: Multiple Choice   Objective: 15-1.3
    Level: I   Tag: None

Each binary digit is called a

        a) bit.   b) byte.

        c) state.   d) code.

a

11) Item Type: Multiple Choice   Objective: 15-1.3
    Level: I   Tag: None

One disadvantage of analog signals is that they

        a) can be sent quickly.   b) can be turned on and off frequently.

        c) get distorted after several transmissions.   d) can transmit a lot of information in a short time.

c

12) Item Type: Multiple Choice   Objective: 15-1.4
    Level: I   Tag: None

Optical fibers

        a) carry signals that are represented by pulses of light.   b) are smaller and lighter than wire cables.

        c) are about 7.6 cm in diameter.   d) both a and b.

d

13) Item Type: Multiple Choice   Objective: 15-1.5
    Level: I   Tag: None

Microwaves are a form of

        a) electric waves.   b) mechanical waves.

        c) sound waves.   d) electromagnetic waves.

d

Chapter 15

14) Item Type: Multiple Choice   Objective: 15-1.5
    Level: I   Tag: None

Microwaves are used for sending telecommunication signals in

        a) fiber-optic networks.   b) wire-cable networks.

        c) underground cables.   d) atmospheric transmission.

d

15) Item Type: Multiple Choice   Objective: 15-1.5
    Level: I   Tag: None

What is a satellite footprint?

    a) the geographic region covered by a communications satellite   b) satellite debris left in space by a communications satellite

    c) the blueprints used to make a communications satellite   d) the geographic region not covered by a communications satellite

a

16) Item Type: Multiple Choice   Objective: 15-2.1
    Level: I   Tag: None

When you talk on the telephone, the sound waves of your voice are converted to an electrical signal by a(n)

        a) conductor.   b) insulator.

        c) transducer.   d) receiver.

c

17) Item Type: Multiple Choice   Objective: 15-2.1
    Level: I   Tag: None

Over the telephone line, the sound waves from your voice are transmitted

        a) without any conversion.   b) as variations in electric current.

        c) as longitudinal waves.   d) as vibrations.

b

18) Item Type: Multiple Choice   Objective: 15-2.1
Level: I   Tag: None

During a telephone call, the incoming electrical signals are converted to sound waves by

      a) electret microphone.   b) fiber optics.

      c) hand set.   d) speaker cone.

d

19) Item Type: Multiple Choice   Objective: 15-2.1
Level: I   Tag: None

The transfer of information by means of electromagnetic waves through space is called

      a) atmospheric transmission.   b) atmospheric radiation.

      c) atmospheric conduction.   d) atmospheric convection.

a

20) Item Type: Multiple Choice   Objective: 15-2.2
Level: I   Tag: None

Telephone messages are sent by

      a) physical transmission only. b) atmospheric transmission
                                      only.

      c) both physical and   d) none of the above
      atmospheric transmissions.

c

21) Item Type: Multiple Choice   Objective: 15-2.2
Level: I   Tag: None

The area covered by each microwave relay antenna mounted on towers is called a

      a) box.   b) cell.

      c) space.   d) region.

b

22) Item Type: Multiple Choice   Objective: 15-2.2
    Level: I   Tag: None

A cordless phone is a

        a) transmitter.   b) receiver.

        c) transceiver.   d) translocator.

c

23) Item Type: Multiple Choice   Objective: 15-2.3
    Level: I   Tag: None

For radio broadcast, sound signals are converted to

        a) ultraviolet waves.   b) infrared waves.

        c) visible light waves.   d) electromagnetic waves.

d

24) Item Type: Multiple Choice   Objective: 15-2.3
    Level: I   Tag: None

The antenna of your radio receiver works as a

        a) transmitter.   b) transducer.

        c) transceiver.   d) translocator.

b

25) Item Type: Multiple Choice   Objective: 15-2.3
    Level: I   Tag: None

Television converts electromagnetic waves into

        a) lights and sound.   b) images and sound.

        c) lights and images.   d) all of the above

b

26) Item Type: Multiple Choice   Objective: 15-2.4
    Level: I   Tag: None

The smallest piece of electronically produced picture is called a

        a) bit.   b) byte.

        c) ray.   d) pixel.

d

27) Item Type: Multiple Choice   Objective: 15-2.4
    Level: I   Tag: None

A cathode-ray tube in a black-and-white TV makes a beam of electrons from

        a) phosphors.   b) a negatively charged cathode.

        c) electromagnetic signals.   d) a television camera.

b

28) Item Type: Multiple 3   Objective: 15-2.4
    Level: I   Tag: None

By the year 2006, all television signals will be broadcast

        a) visually.   b) electromagnetically.

        c) using radio waves.   d) digitally.

d

29) Item Type: Multiple Choice   Objective: 15-3.1
    Level: I   Tag: None

Which of the following is not a computer input device?

        a) a keyboard   b) a mouse

        c) a scanner   d) a printer

d

30) Item Type: Multiple Choice   Objective: 15-3.1
    Level: I   Tag: None

Which of the following is *not* a function of a computer?

        a) input   b) thinking

        c) processing   d) storage

b

31) Item Type: Multiple Choice   Objective: 15-3.1
    Level: I   Tag: None

A computer keyboard is an example of a(n)

        a) input device.   b) output device.

        c) storage device.   d) processing device.

a

32) Item Type: Multiple Choice   Objective: 15-3.1
    Level: I   Tag: None

A computer monitor is an example of a(n)

    a) input device.   b) output device.

    c) storage device.   d) processing device.

b

33) Item Type: Multiple Choice   Objective: 15-3.1
    Level: I   Tag: None

A computer modem is

    a) an input device.   b) an output device.

    c) both an input and output device.   d) neither an input nor an output device.

c

34) Item Type: Multiple Choice   Objective: 15-3.2
    Level: I   Tag: None

All input devices provide data to the computer in the form of a(n)

    a) radio signal.   b) atmospheric signal.

    c) binary code.   d) Morse code.

c

35) Item Type: Multiple Choice   Objective: 15-3.2
    Level: I   Tag: None

Computers process binary data in groups of

    a) eight bits.   b) eight bytes.

    c) ten bits.   d) ten bytes.

a

36) Item Type: Multiple Choice   Objective: 15-3.3
    Level: I   Tag: None

In a computer, the operating system is stored on

    a) hardware.   b) a scanner.

    c) the hard drive.   d) a floppy drive.

c

37) Item Type: Multiple Choice Objective: 15-3.3
Level: I Tag: None

Random-access memory, RAM, is contained on

a) hardware. b) software.

c) microtubules. d) microchips.

d

38) Item Type: Multiple Choice Objective: 15-3.3
Level: I Tag: None

All the physical components of a computer are called

a) hardware. b) software.

c) hard drive. d) floppy drive.

a

39) Item Type: Multiple Choice Objective: 15-3.3
Level: I Tag: None

When a computer is first turned on, the first program executed by the computer is the

a) word processing system. b) operating system.

c) control system. d) experimental system.

b

40) Item Type: Multiple Choice Objective: 15-3.4
Level: I Tag: None

In 1989, the Web was

a) used exclusively by the b) as widely available as it is
U.S. Defense Department. today.

c) used mostly as a resource d) nonexistent.
for scientific information.

c

41) Item Type: Short Answer Objective: 15-1.1
Level: I Tag: None

What is the relationship between signals and codes?

Signals are signs that represent information such as a command, a direction, or a warning.
Codes assign meaning to the signals.

42) Item Type: Short Answer   Objective: 15-1.1
     Level: 1   Tag: None

What does a transducer do?

A transducer converts a signal from one form to another.

43) Item Type: Short Answer   Objective: 15-1.2
     Level: 1   Tag: None

What is telecommunication?

communication by electronic means

44) Item Type: Short Answer   Objective: 15-1.3
     Level: 1   Tag: None

How is a digital signal sent?

A digital signal is sent as a sequence of digits, or discrete units.

45) Item Type: Short Answer   Objective: 15-1.4
     Level: 1   Tag: None

Identify one advantage of using optical fibers instead of metal wires.

Optical fibers are lighter and smaller than metal wires. Even so, optical fibers can carry significantly more conversations than metal wires.

46) Item Type: Short Answer   Objective: 15-1.4
     Level: 1   Tag: None

What is the structural composition of optical fibers?

An optical fiber is a hair-thin transparent strand of glass or plastic.

47) Item Type: Short Answer   Objective: 15-1.5
     Level: 1   Tag: None

How does a microwave relay tower transmit signals?

A tower picks up a signal transmitted by another tower, amplifies it, and retransmits the signal to the next tower.

48) Item Type: Short Answer   Objective: 15-1.5
     Level: 1   Tag: None

What is microwave transmission used for?

Microwave transmission is often used to connect distant places.

49) Item Type: Short Answer   Objective: 15-1.5
      Level: 1   Tag: None

For the microwave signals to be sent from one tower to another, how must the towers be placed in relationship to each other?

> For the microwave signals to be sent from one tower to the next, each tower must be almost visible from the top of the other.

50) Item Type: Short Answer   Objective: 15-1.5
      Level: 1   Tag: None

What power source is used to generate electricity in satellites?

> solar power

51) Item Type: Short Answer   Objective: 15-1.5
      Level: 1   Tag: None

What is a satellite footprint?

> The satellite footprint is the maximum area of land covered by a transmitting antenna of a communications satellite.

52) Item Type: Short Answer   Objective: 15-2.2
      Level: 1   Tag: None

What is a physical transmission?

> A physical transmission is a transmission of a signal using wires, cables, or optical fibers.

53) Item Type: Short Answer   Objective: 15-2.2
      Level: 1   Tag: None

What is the most practical way to send a signal locally?

> The most practical way to send a signal to a local geographic destination is through a physical transmission.

54) Item Type: Short Answer   Objective: 15-2.2
      Level: 1   Tag: None

What is the most practical way to send a long distance telephone signal?

> The most practical way to send a long distance telephone signal is through an atmospheric transmission.

55) Item Type: Short Answer   Objective: 15-2.2
    Level: 1   Tag: None

What communication device allows us to communicate with very distant places via telephone?

> a communication satellite

56) Item Type: Short Answer   Objective: 15-2.3
    Level: 1   Tag: None

What is a carrier?

> A carrier is a continuous wave that can be modulated to send a signal.

57) Item Type: Short Answer   Objective: 15-2.3
    Level: 1   Tag: None

What must sound waves be converted to in order to broadcast a radio transmission?

> Sound waves are converted to electromagnetic waves.

58) Item Type: Short Answer   Objective: 15-2.3
    Level: 1   Tag: None

Which type of radio station can broadcast a signal the greatest distance?

> AM

59) Item Type: Short Answer   Objective: 15-2.3
    Level: 1   Tag: None

Why is there a greater geographic range associated with AM stations than with FM stations?

> FM stations rely on a line-of-sight transmission. The lower frequencies of AM stations are not limited to line-of-sight transmission but can follow the curvature of the Earth. Radio waves at AM frequencies can also be reflected by charged particles in the upper atmosphere to locations hundreds or even thousands of miles away.

60) Item Type: Short Answer   Objective: 15-2.3
    Level: 1   Tag: None

What are you tuning into when you change the channel of your television set?

> You tune into the carrier frequency of the station that you choose.

61) Item Type: Short Answer   Objective: 15-2.3
     Level: 1   Tag: None

What is a cathode-ray tube?

A cathode-ray tube is a tube that uses an electron beam to create a display on a phosphorescent screen.

62) Item Type: Short Answer   Objective: 15-2.4
     Level: 1   Tag: None

What are the three primary colors of light associated with color picture tubes?

red, blue, and green

63) Item Type: Short Answer   Objective: 15-2.4
     Level: 1   Tag: None

What is the function of a shadow mask in a color television?

The shadow mask is a screen with holes which directs the beam of color causing it to strike only the phosphor dot that glows the correct color.

64) Item Type: Short Answer   Objective: 15-3.1
     Level: 1   Tag: None

When were the first electronic computers developed?

during World War II

65) Item Type: Short Answer   Objective: 15-3.1
     Level: 1   Tag: None

What are the four basic functions of a computer?

input, output, processing, and storage

66) Item Type: Short Answer   Objective: 15-3.1
     Level: 1   Tag: None

Is a joystick an input or output device?

A joystick is a type of input device.

67) Item Type: Short Answer   Objective: 15-3.2
     Level: 1   Tag: None

What is a logic gate?

A logic gate is an electronic switch that opens and closes circuits within the computer.

Chapter 15

68) Item Type: Short Answer   Objective: 15-3.2
    Level: I   Tag: None

    What does an AND gate do?

    An AND gate closes the circuit and allows current to pass only when both inputs are in the "on" position.

69) Item Type: Short Answer   Objective: 15-3.2
    Level: I   Tag: None

    What does read-only memory do on a computer?

    It is for long-term storage of operating instructions.

70) Item Type: Short Answer   Objective: 15-3.2
    Level: I   Tag: None

    What is the relationship between bits and bytes?

    A bit is represented as 1 or 0. A byte is a group of eight bits.

71) Item Type: Short Answer   Objective: 15-3.3
    Level: I   Tag: None

    What are both hard drives and floppy drives coated with?

    a magnetizable substance on which data is recorded

72) Item Type: Short Answer   Objective: 15-3.3
    Level: I   Tag: None

    What determines the time to access data from the hard drive?

    The time required to access data depends on where the information is stored on the disk and the position of the read-write head.

73) Item Type: Short Answer   Objective: 15-3.3
    Level: II   Tag: None

    What do the transistors on a memory chip do?

    The transistors on a memory chip function as two-position switches allowing the computer to operate as a binary machine.

74) Item Type: Short Answer   Objective: 15-3.3
    Level: I   Tag: None

    What does software provide?

    Software provides instructions to carry out desired tasks.

Copyright© by Holt, Rinehart and Winston. All rights reserved.

253

75) Item Type: Essay   Objective: 15-1.2
     Level: II   Tag: None

Describe how a microphone and speaker work together to produce amplified sound.

> The sound waves move into a microphone where they are converted to an electric signal. The signal travels through a wire in the form of an electric current. In the speaker, the electric signal is amplified and converted back into sound.

76) Item Type: Essay   Objective: 15-1.3
     Level: II   Tag: None

How is music read from a compact disc?

> A laser beam shines on the disc. The detector receives light reflected from the smooth areas of the disc. The reflected light represents the music written as a binary code on the disc. This digital information is converted into sound through the speaker.

77) Item Type: Essay   Objective: 15-1.5
     Level: II   Tag: None

Is a geostationary satellite really stationary? Explain.

> No. A geostationary satellite appears stationary because it orbits Earth at the same rate that Earth rotates; therefore the satellite does not appear to move.

78) Item Type: Essay   Objective: 15-2.1
     Level: II   Tag: None

Where are electret microphones found and how do they work?

> Electret microphones are found in newer phones. An electrically charged membrane transforms sound waves into an analog electrical signal.

79) Item Type: Essay   Objective: 15-3.3
     Level: II   Tag: None

Compare and contrast RAM and ROM.

> RAM and ROM refer to two types of memory within a computer. Random-access memory, RAM, is used for short-term storage of data and instructions. Any of the data in RAM can be accessed in the same time. Read-only memory, ROM, is permanently stored when the chip is manufactured. The information stored here cannot be altered.

80) Item Type: Essay   Objective: 15-1.3
Level: III   Tag: None

Identify each of the following examples as being either digital or analog in nature. For each example, explain your reasoning.

a. the sound from an electric guitar
b. a television signal
c. a message in Morse code
d. a compact disc
e. a phonograph record

a. Analog; a pickup converts the vibrations of the guitar string into electrical signals; these are converted by the amplifier.
b. Analog; a television signal is similar to a radio signal (which is analog), but it contains more information.
c. Digital; the dots and dashes of Morse code are like ones and zeros; the specific combination of dots and dashes denotes letters or numbers.
d. Digital; the CD encodes information as ones (pits) or zeros (blanks)
e. Analog; the vibrations of sound are represented as tiny ridges in the grooves of the record. The rubbing of the needle across these ridges creates an electrical signal that is amplified to recreate the original sound.

81) Item Type: Essay   Objective: 15-1.3
Level: III   Tag: None

Kim placed the computer diskette containing her term paper on top of the microwave while she heated a bowl of soup. When later she tried to work on her paper, the computer flashed an error message indicating that it could not read the disk. What happened?

Computer diskettes are similar to video and audiotapes in that they contain magnetic material that is arranged in specific ways to encode information. Microwaves contain strong magnets. Placing the diskette in the microwave's magnetic field disrupted the magnetic pattern of the diskette, destroying the information on the diskette.

Chapter 16

1) Item Type: Multiple Choice   Objective: 16-1.1
   Level: I   Tag: None

   The number of universes known to exist is

   a) one.   b) two.

   c) three.   d) four.

   a

2) Item Type: Multiple Choice   Objective: 16-1.2
   Level: I   Tag: None

   A light-year is

   a) a unit of time.   b) a unit of distance.

   c) a unit of mass.   d) a unit of density.

   b

3) Item Type: Multiple Choice   Objective: 16-1.2
   Level: I   Tag: None

   Not including the sun, the closest stars to Earth are

   a) 4.3 light-years away.   b) 43 light-years away.

   c) 430 light-years away.   d) 4300 light-years away.

   a

4) Item Type: Multiple Choice   Objective: 16-1.3
   Level: I   Tag: None

   Our solar system is inside the

   a) Alpha Centauri galaxy.   b) Betelgeuse galaxy.

   c) Milky Way galaxy.   d) Andromeda galaxy.

   c

5) Item Type: Multiple Choice   Objective: 16-1.3
   Level: II   Tag: None

   Astronomers estimate that the universe contains

   a) 100 galaxies.   b) 100 million galaxies.

   c) 100 billion galaxies.   d) 100 trillion galaxies.

   c

6) Item Type: Multiple Choice   Objective: 16-1.3
    Level: I   Tag: None

The Milky Way galaxy contains interstellar matter that may

        a) form new galaxies.   b) form new stars.

        c) form new universes.   d) form new constellations.

b

7) Item Type: Multiple Choice   Objective: 16-1.4
    Level: I   Tag: None

Galaxies are classified based on their

        a) shape.   b) color.

        c) stars.   d) age.

a

8) Item Type: Multiple Choice   Objective: 16-1.4
    Level: II   Tag: None

Spiral galaxies often appear bluish due to an abundance of

        a) old stars.   b) black holes.

        c) young stars.   d) white dwarfs.

c

9) Item Type: Multiple Choice   Objective: 16-1.4
    Level: I   Tag: None

Elliptical galaxies often appear reddish due to an abundance of

        a) old stars.   b) black holes.

        c) young stars.   d) white dwarfs.

a

10) Item Type: Multiple Choice   Objective: 16-1.4
    Level: I   Tag: None

Our galaxy is classified as a(n)

        a) irregular galaxy.   b) elliptical galaxy.

        c) spherical galaxy.   d) spiral galaxy.

d

11) Item Type: Multiple Choice   Objective: 16-1.5
    Level: I   Tag: None

Clusters of galaxies can form larger groups called

        a) supernovas.   b) superclusters.

        c) constellations.   d) supergiants.

b

12) Item Type: Multiple Choice   Objective: 16-1.5
    Level: I   Tag: None

Who first proposed that the universe is expanding?

        a) Darwin   b) Kepler

        c) Copernicus   d) Hubble

d

13) Item Type: Multiple Choice   Objective: 16-1.5
    Level: I   Tag: None

An observation of the red shift of galaxies suggests that the universe is

        a) expanding.   b) contracting.

        c) reversing.   d) stagnant.

a

14) Item Type: Multiple Choice   Objective: 16-1.5
    Level: I   Tag: None

The big bang theory states that the universe began with a gigantic explosion

        a) 4.4 billion years ago.   b) 10 to 20 billion years ago.

        c) 50 billion years ago.   d) 100 billion years ago.

b

15) Item Type: Multiple Choice   Objective: 16-2.1
    Level: I   Tag: None

All stars

        a) reflect light from the sun.   b) appear to wander off their
                                                    star paths.

        c) produce their own light.   d) all of the above

c

16) Item Type: Multiple Choice   Objective: 16-2.1
    Level: I   Tag: None

All stars

    a) radiate heat energy.   b) radiate electromagnetic waves.

    c) radiate light energy.   d) all of the above

d

17) Item Type: Multiple Choice   Objective: 16-2.2
    Level: I   Tag: None

The surface temperature of a star can be estimated based on the star's

    a) size.   b) color.

    c) age.   d) mass.

b

18) Item Type: Multiple Choice   Objective: 16-2.2
    Level: I   Tag: None

A star's apparent brightness is dependent upon

    a) temperature.   b) distance from Earth.

    c) size.   d) all of the above

d

19) Item Type: Multiple Choice   Objective: 16-2.2
    Level: I   Tag: None

Hotter stars glow with light that is more intense at

    a) shorter wavelengths (toward the red end of the spectrum).   b) shorter wavelengths (toward the blue end of the spectrum).

    c) longer wavelengths (toward the red end of the spectrum).   d) longer wavelengths (toward the blue end of the spectrum).

b

Chapter 16

20) Item Type: Multiple Choice   Objective: 16-2.2
    Level: I   Tag: None

The sun is

a) an unusually hot star.   b) a very cool star.

c) a typical star.   d) none of the above

c

21) Item Type: Multiple Choice   Objective: 16-2.3
    Level: I   Tag: None

Stars are held together by

a) ionic forces.   b) magnetic forces.

c) electrical forces.   d) gravitational forces.

d

22) Item Type: Multiple Choice   Objective: 16-2.3
    Level: I   Tag: None

In stars, energy is produced primarily as hydrogen atoms are combined to form

a) helium atoms.   b) carbon atoms.

c) oxygen atoms.   d) nitrogen atoms.

a

23) Item Type: Multiple Choice   Objective: 16-2.3
    Level: I   Tag: None

Energy is released in stars as a result of

a) fission reactions.   b) fusion reactions.

c) endothermic reactions.   d) biochemical reactions.

b

24) Item Type: Multiple Choice   Objective: 16-2.4
    Level: I   Tag: None

Nearly 90 percent of all stars are at what point in their life cycles?

a) infancy   b) youth

c) mid-life   d) old age

c

25) Item Type: Multiple Choice   Objective: 16-2.4
    Level: I   Tag: None

A star is born when

        a) gas and dust collapse inward.   b) nuclear fusion starts in the core.

        c) the fusion of hydrogen slows down.   d) the core becomes carbon and oxygen.

b

26) Item Type: Multiple Choice   Objective: 16-2.4
    Level: II   Tag: None

Supergiant stars

        a) form from red giants.   b) fuse hydrogen into carbon.

        c) form planetary nebula.   d) form supernovas.

d

27) Item Type: Multiple Choice   Objective: 16-2.4
    Level: I   Tag: None

Most of the stars in the Milky Way will end their lives as

        a) white dwarfs.   b) black holes.

        c) supernovas.   d) red giants.

a

28) Item Type: Multiple Choice   Objective: 16-3.1
    Level: I   Tag: None

_____ first proposed that Earth and the other planets orbit the sun.

        a) Hubble   b) Galileo

        c) Copernicus   d) Kepler

c

29) Item Type: Multiple Choice   Objective: 16-3.1
    Level: I   Tag: None

Kepler showed that the orbits of the planets are

        a) circular.   b) elliptical.

        c) irregular.   d) none of the above

b

30) Item Type: Multiple Choice   Objective: 16-3.1
    Level: I   Tag: None

Besides the sun and the moon, what is the brightest object in the sky?

        a) Sirius   b) Venus

        c) Jupiter   d) Orion

b

31) Item Type: Multiple Choice   Objective: 16-3.1
    Level: I   Tag: None

All of the planets in our solar system

        a) give off their own light.   b) appear in the same position nightly.

        c) have thick atmospheres.   d) orbit the sun.

d

32) Item Type: Multiple Choice   Objective: 16-3.1
    Level: I   Tag: None

Which of the following is *not* an inner planet?

        a) Mars   b) Jupiter

        c) Venus   d) Earth

b

Chapter 16

33) Item Type: Multiple Choice   Objective: 16-3.1
      Level: I   Tag: None

Mercury is characterized by

      a) a thick atmosphere.   b) large volumes of water.

      c) very extreme temperatures.   d) high atmospheric pressure at its surface.

c

34) Item Type: Multiple Choice   Objective: 16-3.1
      Level: I   Tag: None

The inner planets are separated from the outer planets by

      a) Orion's belt.   b) an asteroid belt.

      c) the Milky Way.   d) the moon's orbit.

b

35) Item Type: Multiple Choice   Objective: 16-3.1
      Level: I   Tag: None

The Great Red Spot is believed to be a giant storm in the atmosphere of

      a) Mars.   b) Jupiter.

      c) Saturn.   d) Neptune.

b

36) Item Type: Multiple Choice   Objective: 16-3.1
      Level: I   Tag: None

Which of the following does *not* have rings?

      a) Uranus   b) Mars

      c) Jupiter   d) Neptune

b

37) Item Type: Multiple Choice   Objective: 16-3.2
      Level: I   Tag: None

The most widely accepted model of the formation of the solar system is the

      a) nebular model.   b) heliocentric model.

      c) big bang theory.   d) geologic model.

a

Chapter 16

38) Item Type: Multiple Choice   Objective: 16-3.2
    Level: I   Tag: None

Planets may have formed out of material orbiting the early sun through the process of

a) solidification.   b) sedimentation.

c) accretion.   d) radiation.

c

39) Item Type: Multiple Choice   Objective: 16-3.3
    Level: I   Tag: None

The phases of the moon are determined by

a) the relative positions of   b) the relative positions of the
Earth and moon.   sun and moon.

c) the relative positions of   d) the relative positions of
Earth and sun.   Earth, sun, and moon.

d

40) Item Type: Multiple Choice   Objective: 16-3.3
    Level: I   Tag: None

During a solar eclipse

a) the moon blocks out the   b) the sun blocks out the
sun.   moon.

c) the moon blocks out Earth.   d) Earth blocks out the sun.

a

41) Item Type: Short Answer   Objective: 16-1.1
    Level: II   Tag: None

Define *universe*.

The universe is defined as everything physical that exists in space and time, including all
matter and energy that exists, now, in the past, and in the future.

42) Item Type: Short Answer   Objective: 16-1.2
    Level: I   Tag: None

What is a light-year?

A light-year is the distance that light can travel in one year.

43) Item Type: Short Answer   Objective: 16-1.2
     Level: II   Tag: None

Why is a light-year a more useful measurement in astronomy than a meter is?

> The enormous size of the galaxy and universe necessitate a much larger unit of measure than is provided by the meter. If meters were the standard unit of measure, numeric representations of distances between celestial bodies would be so large as to be impractical.

44) Item Type: Short Answer   Objective: 16-1.3
     Level: I   Tag: None

Where in the Milky Way galaxy is our solar system located?

> Our solar system is located inside the Milky Way galaxy about midway between the galaxy's edge and its center.

45) Item Type: Short Answer   Objective: 16-1.4
     Level: II   Tag: None

What are some physical characteristics of elliptical galaxies?

> Elliptical galaxies are egg-shaped galaxies without spiral arms or interstellar gas and dust. They usually contain many older stars, so they often have a reddish tint.

46) Item Type: Short Answer   Objective: None
     Level: None   Tag: None

What are some physical characteristics of a spiral galaxy?

> Spiral galaxies are disk-shaped galaxies with a central bulge and spiral arms of gas and dust. They usually contain many young stars, so they often have a bluish tint.

47) Item Type: Short Answer   Objective: 16-1.4
     Level: I   Tag: None

How are irregular galaxies different from spiral and elliptical galaxies?

> Whereas both spiral and elliptical galaxies have well-defined shapes and structures, irregular galaxies do not.

48) Item Type: Short Answer   Objective: 16-1.4
     Level: I   Tag: None

What force is theorized to hold the universe together?

> Gravity. Because of gravity, stars, gas, and dust collect into larger units called galaxies, and galaxies group into clusters and superclusters.

49) Item Type: Short Answer   Objective: 16-1.5
     Level: 1   Tag: None

What is the big bang theory?

> The big bang theory is a scientific theory describing the origin of the universe in a gigantic explosion sometime between 10 and 20 billion years ago.

50) Item Type: Short Answer   Objective: 16-1.5
     Level: 1   Tag: None

What evidence was discovered in 1965 that supports the big bang theory?

> If the beginning of the universe had happened as outlined in the big bang theory, then remnants of the explosion should exist as radiation at microwave wavelengths. Scientists believe that they found these remnants when they detected *cosmic background radiation* in 1965.

51) Item Type: Short Answer   Objective: 16-2.1
     Level: 1   Tag: None

Name two properties that are used to characterize a star.

> Two defining properties used to characterize a star are color and brightness. Also, composition, and the fact that stars are driven by nuclear fusion reactions.

52) Item Type: Short Answer   Objective: 16-2.1
     Level: 1   Tag: None

What information can be derived from the color of a star?

> Each color is associated with a specific temperature. Therefore, the surface temperature of a star can be estimated using color.

53) Item Type: Short Answer   Objective: 16-2.2
     Level: 1   Tag: None

How do we gather information about distant stars?

> We gather information about stars using the light that is produced by each star.

54) Item Type: Short Answer   Objective: 16-2.2
     Level: 1   Tag: None

What is the primary instrument used to gather information about stars?

> The telescope is the primary instrument used to gather information about stars.

55) Item Type: Short Answer   Objective: 16-2.3
Level: 1   Tag: None

What is a fusion reaction?

A fusion reaction is a nuclear reaction in which two lighter nuclei combine to form a heavier nucleus.

56) Item Type: Short Answer   Objective: 16-2.3
Level: 1   Tag: None

What environmental conditions, common to most stars including our sun, appear to be necessary in order for fusion reactions to take place?

Nuclear fusion occurs under conditions of extremely high temperature and pressure.

57) Item Type: Short Answer   Objective: 16-2.3
Level: 1   Tag: None

What are the products and reactants in the primary fusion reaction carried out within the sun?

Two hydrogen nuclei are fused to produce a helium nucleus and energy.

58) Item Type: Short Answer   Objective: 16-2.4
Level: 1   Tag: None

How much longer is our sun expected to live?

The sun is estimated to have enough fuel to carry out nuclear fusion for another 5 billion years.

59) Item Type: Short Answer   Objective: 16-2.4
Level: 1   Tag: None

What is a planetary nebula?

A planetary nebula is a glowing cloud or ring of gas produced as a dying average-sized star expands outward from its core.

60) Item Type: Short Answer   Objective: 16-2.4
Level: 1   Tag: None

What is a supernova?

A supernova is a violent explosion that occurs when the core of a very large star has turned completely to iron.

61) Item Type: Short Answer   Objective: 16-2.4
    Level: I   Tag: None

When is a white dwarf formed?

At the end of the life cycle of medium and small stars.

62) Item Type: Short Answer   Objective: 16-2.4
    Level: I   Tag: None

What is a neutron star?

A neutron star is a dead star with the density of atomic nuclei.

63) Item Type: Short Answer   Objective: 16-3.1
    Level: I   Tag: None

Prior to the work of Copernicus in 1543, what did a model of the universe look like?

Old maps of the universe show the sun, moon, and planets orbiting Earth in perfect circles.

64) Item Type: Short Answer   Objective: 16-3.1
    Level: I   Tag: None

Who is credited with describing the orbits of the planets as elliptical?

Following Copernicus's work establishing the sun as the center of the solar system, Kepler showed that the orbital paths of the planets were elliptical.

65) Item Type: Short Answer   Objective: 16-3.1
    Level: II   Tag: None

Which planet's atmosphere is characterized by the presence of carbon dioxide and sulfuric acid?

Venus's atmosphere contains high concentrations of carbon dioxide and sulfuric acid.

66) Item Type: Short Answer   Objective: 16-3.1
    Level: I   Tag: None

What is the brightest object in the night sky? Why?

Venus appears bright in the night sky because it is close to Earth and it has a thick atmosphere that reflects sunlight very well.

67) Item Type: Short Answer   Objective: 16-3.1
    Level: I   Tag: None

Why are planets in other solar systems difficult to detect?

Planets in other solar systems are difficult to detect because planets do not give off their own light.

68) Item Type: Short Answer   Objective: 16-3.1
     Level: 1   Tag: None

What is the source of most of our current knowledge of Mercury's appearance and geology?

> Much of our knowledge of Mercury comes from the *Mariner 10* space mission in 1974.

69) Item Type: Short Answer   Objective: 16-3.1
     Level: 1   Tag: None

What are asteroids and where are they located?

> Asteroids are small rocky objects that orbit the sun, usually in a band between Mars and Jupiter.

70) Item Type: Short Answer   Objective: 16-3.1
     Level: 1   Tag: None

What is *Galileo*?

> *Galileo* is a spacecraft that was launched in 1989 with the goal of gathering information about the physical properties of the outer planets.

71) Item Type: Short Answer   Objective: 16-3.1
     Level: 1   Tag: None

What makes Pluto's orbit unique?

> Pluto's orbit is not on a plane with those of the other planets. Pluto's elliptical orbit periodically cuts inside the orbit of Neptune.

72) Item Type: Short Answer   Objective: 16-3.2
     Level: 1   Tag: None

From what kind of evidence is the age of the universe inferred?

> Geologic dating of rocks from Earth, the moon, and asteroids has been used to infer the age of the solar system.

73) Item Type: Short Answer   Objective: 16-3.2
     Level: 1   Tag: None

What widely accepted scientific model describes the formation of the solar system?

> The nebular model describes the formation of the solar system.

74) Item Type: Short Answer   Objective: 16-3.2
    Level: I   Tag: None

How are planets believed to have formed?

Planets are believed to have formed through the accretion of material orbiting the early sun.

75) Item Type: Short Answer   Objective: 16-3.3
    Level: I   Tag: None

How many satellites does Earth have? Explain your answer.

Earth has one natural satellite, the moon. [Students may include man-made satellites as well. Accept all reasonable answers in accord with the definition of a satellite as any body that orbits another, either natural or man-made.]

76) Item Type: Short Answer   Objective: 16-3.3
    Level: I   Tag: None

What phase is the moon in when only a small portion of the moon is visible?

The moon is in a crescent phase when only a small portion of the moon is visible.

77) Item Type: Essay   Objective: 16-2.2
    Level: II   Tag: None

Describe how astronomers determine the composition of a star.

When a light passes through a prism, the light is broken up into different colors. Each color corresponds to a specific wavelength in the electromagnetic spectrum. Each element produces a unique pattern of spectral lines, which includes dark lines where light is missing at specific wavelengths. By comparing the spectral line patterns of known elements to those produced by stars, scientists can deduce the chemical composition of stars.

78) Item Type: Essay   Objective: 16-2.3
    Level: II   Tag: None

Describe the birth of a star.

A star begins to form when a cloud of gas and dust collapses inward as a result of gravitational forces. When the temperature at the center of the cloud reaches approximately 15 million Kelvins, electrons are stripped from hydrogen atoms, leaving positively charged protons. At these very high temperatures, protons can fuse to form helium atoms. Once nuclear fusion begins in the cloud, a star is born.

79) Item Type: Essay   Objective: 16-2.4
    Level: II   Tag: None

How is the death of a very large star different from the death of smaller stars?

Late in their lives, smaller stars become red giants that fuse helium into carbon and oxygen. Then they die out as white dwarfs. Rather than red giants, large stars form supergiants that can produce iron through fusion. When the core of a supergiant is entirely iron, fusion stops, which causes the core to collapse. This collapse results in a violent rebound explosion called a supernova.

80) Item Type: Essay   Objective: 16-2.4
    Level: II   Tag: None

Why do some stars form white dwarfs and other stars form black holes?

Whether a star forms a white dwarf or a black hole depends on the mass of the dying star. Once the supply of hydrogen atoms in their cores has been converted to helium, small and medium-sized stars will convert helium into carbon and oxygen. A carbon/oxygen core leads to the eventual production of a white dwarf. However, due to high core temperatures in large stars, they can produce elements as heavy as iron. When the core is entirely iron, the star explodes in a supernova. If the mass of the star's core after a supernova is greater than three times that of the sun, the core collapses, forming a black hole.

81) Item Type: Essay   Objective: 16-3.1
    Level: II   Tag: None

Compare and contrast planets and stars.

Although both planets and stars appear as points of light in the night sky and appear to cross the sky in the same direction, their similarities end there. Stars produce their own light. Clouds associated with and the surfaces of planets reflect the light of the sun. Stars appear to cross the sky in the same star path night after night. Planets "wander" from their paths against the background of stars. Because they are much closer than stars, planets appear through a telescope as disks rather than mere points of light.

82) Item Type: Thinking Critically   Objective: 16-2.1
    Level: III   Tag: None

A constellation is a group of stars appearing in a pattern as seen from Earth. The stars in the constellation Orion appear close together in the sky although they are actually quite far away from each other. Why do the stars in the night sky all appear to be the same distance away from the surface of Earth?

The closest stars to Earth are more than 4 light-years away. All other stars are farther than 4 light-years away. Because the distance between the surface of Earth and stars is so great, our depth perception fails to discriminate between distances in individual stars. Stars appear to be projected, equidistant, from the surface of Earth onto the celestial sphere that encircles Earth.

83) Item Type: Thinking Critically   Objective: 16-2.2
     Level: III   Tag: None

Our sun is approximately 93 million miles away, a distance easily covered by modern space probes. Why don't we gather information directly from the sun using probes?

The surface temperature of the sun exceeds 6000 K. No materials presently known on Earth can withstand those temperatures long enough to gather information.

1) Item Type: Multiple Choice   Objective: 17-1.1
   Level: I   Tag: None

The continental crust is deepest beneath

    a) oceans.   b) mountains.

    c) valleys.   d) rivers.

b

2) Item Type: Multiple Choice   Objective: 17-1.1
   Level: II   Tag: None

Oceanic crust is

    a) thicker and less dense than   b) thinner and less dense than
    continental crust.   continental crust.

    c) thicker and more dense than   d) thinner and more dense
    continental crust.   than continental crust.

d

3) Item Type: Multiple Choice   Objective: 17-1.1
   Level: I   Tag: None

About 80 percent of Earth's volume is made up of

    a) crust.   b) mantle.

    c) inner core.   d) outer core.

b

4) Item Type: Multiple Choice   Objective: 17-1.1
   Level: I   Tag: None

Earth's inner core is

    a) hot and solid.   b) hot and liquid.

    c) cool and solid.   d) cool and liquid.

a

5) Item Type: Multiple Choice   Objective: 17-1.2
Level: I   Tag: None

Earth's lithosphere is composed of

         a) the crust only.   b) the mantle only.

         c) the crust and the upper   d) the mantle and the upper
           portion of the mantle.   portion of the outer core.

c

6) Item Type: Multiple Choice   Objective: 17-1.2
Level: I   Tag: None

One hypothesis states that plate movement results from convection currents in the

         a) mantle.   b) asthenosphere.

         c) lithosphere.   d) outer core.

b

7) Item Type: Multiple Choice   Objective: 17-1.3
Level: I   Tag: None

A geologic feature of divergent plate boundaries in oceanic crust is the formation of

         a) trenches.   b) fossils.

         c) U-shaped valleys.   d) rift valleys.

d

8) Item Type: Multiple Choice   Objective: 17-1.3
Level: I   Tag: None

A divergent boundary occurs where two plates

         a) move toward each other.   b) move away from each other.

         c) move past each other.   d) move over each other.

b

9) Item Type: Multiple Choice   Objective: 17-1.3
Level: I   Tag: None

A zone where oceanic crust dives beneath continental crust is called a zone of

         a) subduction.   b) divergence.

         c) reduction.   d) rifting.

a

10) Item Type: Multiple Choice   Objective: 17-1.3
Level: I   Tag: None

A convergent boundary occurs where two plates

       a) move toward each other.   b) move away from each other.

       c) move past each other.   d) move over each other.

a

11) Item Type: Multiple Choice   Objective: 17-1.3
Level: I   Tag: None

A transform fault boundary occurs where two plates

       a) move toward each other.   b) move away from each other.

       c) move past each other.   d) move over each other.

c

12) Item Type: Multiple Choice   Objective: 17-1.4
Level: I   Tag: None

The reversal of Earth's magnetic poles, as indicated by the rock on the ocean floor, occurs on average every

       a) 100 000 years.   b) 200 000 years.

       c) 300 000 years   d) 400 000 years

b

13) Item Type: Multiple Choice   Objective: 17-2.1
Level: I   Tag: None

Earthquakes occur mostly

       a) in the middle of continents.   b) in the asthenosphere.

       c) at plate boundaries.   d) at the edges of the continents.

c

14) Item Type: Multiple Choice   Objective: 17-2.1
Level: I   Tag: None

The breakage of rocks along a fault line releases energy in the form of

       a) P waves.   b) seismic waves.

       c) heat.   d) light.

b

15) Item Type: Multiple Choice   Objective: 17-2.2
    Level: I   Tag: None

Longitudinal waves

        a) travel the fastest.   b) cannot be detected in locations between 105° and 140° from an earthquake's epicenter.

        c) travel through solids and liquids.   d) all of the above

d

---

16) Item Type: Multiple Choice   Objective: 17-2.2
    Level: I   Tag: None

Which of the following is *not* a characteristic of S waves?

        a) travel slower than P waves.   b) cannot be detected in locations more than 105° from an earthquake's epicenter.

        c) travel through solids and liquids.   d) only affect coastal regions.

c

---

17) Item Type: Multiple Choice   Objective: 17-2.2
    Level: I   Tag: None

Waves that cause the most damage during an earthquake are

        a) surface waves.   b) P waves.

        c) S waves.   d) ocean waves.

a

---

18) Item Type: Multiple Choice   Objective: 17-2.3
    Level: I   Tag: None

A seismograph measures

        a) how much the surface of Earth moves during an earthquake.   b) the speed of S waves.

        c) the force of the earthquake.   d) the location of the epicenter.

a

19) Item Type: Multiple Choice   Objective: 17-2.3
Level: I   Tag: None

The minimum number of seismograph stations necessary to determine the location of an earthquake's epicenter is

    a) one.   b) two.

    c) three.   d) four.

c

20) Item Type: Multiple Choice   Objective: 17-2.3
Level: I   Tag: None

Scientists can calculate the distance from the seismograph station to the focus using

    a) the difference in arrival times of P and surface waves.   b) the difference in arrival times of P and S waves.

    c) the difference in arrival times of S and surface waves.   d) none of the above

b

21) Item Type: Multiple Choice   Objective: 17-2.3
Level: I   Tag: None

The magnitude of earthquakes is expressed using

    a) the Richter scale.   b) the Mercalli scale.

    c) the amplitude of the P waves.   d) the Mohs' scale.

a

22) Item Type: Multiple Choice   Objective: 17-2.4
Level: I   Tag: None

The magma released from volcanoes is

    a) material from the core.   b) molten rocks from the mantle and crust.

    c) liquid iron and nickel.   d) radioactive.

b

23) Item Type: Multiple Choice   Objective: 17-2.5
Level: I   Tag: None

The magma of shield volcanoes is rich in

    a) nitrogen and oxygen.   b) magnesium and iron.

    c) silica.   d) hydrogen.

b

24) Item Type: Multiple Choice   Objective: 17-2.5
Level: I   Tag: None

A cinder cone volcano is caused by

    a) converging plates.   b) diverging plates.

    c) large amounts of gas   d) vents.
    trapped in the magma.

c

25) Item Type: Multiple Choice   Objective: 17-2.5
Level: I   Tag: None

Composite volcanoes are made up of

    a) many layers of cinders and   b) many layers of lava rich in
    lava.   magnesium and iron.

    c) many layers of cinders.   d) many layers of
        metamorphic rock.

a

26) Item Type: Multiple Choice   Objective: 17-3.1
Level: II   Tag: None

A mineral

    a) has a chemical formula.   b) occurs naturally.

    c) has a characteristic internal   d) all of the above
    structure.

d

27) Item Type: Multiple Choice   Objective: 17-3.1
Level: I   Tag: None

Which of the following is not among the nine most common rock forming minerals?

    a) calcite   b) gold

    c) feldspar   d) quartz

b

28) Item Type: Multiple Choice   Objective: 17-3.1
Level: II   Tag: None

Which of the following is *not* a rock?

    a) granite   b) shale

    c) marble   d) diamond

d

29) Item Type: Multiple Choice   Objective: 17-3.1
Level: I   Tag: None

Which of the following is *not* a rock type?

    a) igneous   b) sedimentary

    c) cubic   d) metamorphic

c

30) Item Type: Multiple Choice   Objective: 17-3.2
Level: I   Tag: None

Igneous rock forms from

    a) weathered rock particles.   b) evaporation of water.

    c) magma.   d) none of the above

c

31) Item Type: Multiple Choice   Objective: 17-3.2
Level: I   Tag: None

Sedimentary rocks are the only rocks that can potentially contain

    a) fossils.   b) minerals.

    c) fractures.   d) faults.

a

32) Item Type: Multiple Choice   Objective: 17-3.2
Level: None   Tag: None

Igneous rocks that have mineral crystals easily seen with the unaided eye formed

a) extrusively.   b) intrusively.

c) under water.   d) through compaction.

b

33) Item Type: Multiple Choice   Objective: 17-3.2
Level: I   Tag: None

Sedimentary rocks are named according to

a) the type of minerals they   b) where they were formed.
contain.

c) when they were formed.   d) the size of the fragments they
contain.

d

34) Item Type: Multiple Choice   Objective: 17-3.2
Level: I   Tag: None

Limestone can be metamorphosed into

a) gneiss   b) shale

c) marble   d) slate

c

35) Item Type: Multiple Choice   Objective: 17-3.2
Level: I   Tag: None

Which type of rock is formed from weathering?

a) metamorphic rock   b) magma

c) igneous rock   d) minerals

a

36) Item Type: Multiple Choice   Objective: 17-3.3
Level: II   Tag: None

Rocks that are changed by heat and pressure will form

a) sedimentary rocks.   b) metamorphic rocks.

c) igneous rocks.   d) magma.

b

37) Item Type: Multiple Choice   Objective: 17-3.3
    Level: II   Tag: Rock cycle

The rock labeled "B" is

      a) igneous.   b) metamorphic.

      c) sedimentary.   d) magma.

a

38) Item Type: Multiple Choice   Objective: 17-3.3
    Level: None   Tag: Rock cycle

The rock labeled "A" is

      a) igneous.   b) metamorphic.

      c) sedimentary.   d) magma.

c

39) Item Type: Multiple Choice   Objective: 17-3.4
    Level: I   Tag: Rock cycle

The principle of superposition is used to

      a) determine the absolute age   b) determine how rocks are
      of rocks.   formed.

      c) determine the relative age of   d) determine how rocks are
      rocks.   changed.

c

40) Item Type: Multiple Choice   Objective: 17-3.4
    Level: I   Tag: None

Radioactive isotopes are used to

      a) determine the absolute age   b) determine the relative age
      of rocks.   of rocks.

      c) determine how rocks are   d) determine how rocks are
      formed.   changed.

a

41) Item Type: Multiple Choice   Objective: 17-4.1
    Level: I   Tag: None

Weathering that does *not* alter the chemical composition of the rock is called

      a) chemical weathering.   b) physical weathering.

      c) biological weathering.   d) acid weathering.

b

42) Item Type: Multiple Choice   Objective: 17-4.1
    Level: I   Tag: None

The most effective agent of physical weathering and erosion is

        a) water.   b) wind.

        c) gravity.   d) plant roots.

a

43) Item Type: Multiple Choice   Objective: 17-4.1
    Level: I   Tag: None

The process in which sediment is laid down is called

        a) erosion.   b) deposition.

        c) weathering.   d) cementation.

b

44) Item Type: Multiple Choice   Objective: 17-4.1
    Level: I   Tag: valley

Which of the following valley shapes would glaciers produce?

        a) A   b) B

        c) C   d) D

a

45) Item Type: Multiple Choice   Objective: 17-4.2
    Level: I   Tag: None

Carbonic acid dissolved in water is a

        a) physical weathering agent.   b) chemical weathering agent.

        c) biological weathering agent.   d) mechanical weathering
                                       agent.

b

46) Item Type: Multiple Choice   Objective: 17-4.2
    Level: I   Tag: None

Underground limestone caves form

a) from cooling and solidification of magma below the surface.

b) from the compacting and cementing of weathered rock fragments.

c) oxidation decomposes the minerals in the rock.

d) when the calcite is dissolved by carbonic acid in rainwater.

d

47) Item Type: Multiple Choice   Objective: 17-4.3
    Level: II   Tag: None

Rain is naturally

a) slightly acidic.

b) very acidic.

c) slightly basic.

d) very basic.

a

48) Item Type: Short Answer   Objective: 17-1.1
    Level: II   Tag: None

Is Earth's crust the same density and thickness throughout? Explain your answer.

No. There are two types of crust; dense, oceanic crust is found beneath the oceans and has a thickness of approximately 4–7 km. Continental crust is thicker and less dense. Continental crust has an average thickness of approximately 20–40 km.

49) Item Type: Short Answer   Objective: 17-1.1
    Level: I   Tag: None

Using your knowledge of temperature and pressure, explain why the inner core of Earth is solid.

The high temperatures of the interior of Earth would normally produce a liquid, however, due to very high pressure, particles that would normally be in a liquid state are forced into a solid state.

50) Item Type: Short Answer   Objective: 17-1.1
    Level: I   Tag: None

How do the materials of the three major compositional layers of Earth differ?

The crust and mantle are both made of hard solid rock, but the crust is less dense than the mantle. The core is believed to be composed of iron and nickel.

51) Item Type: Short Answer   Objective: 17-1.2
Level: 1   Tag: None

What did Alfred Wegener theorize?

> He proposed that based on physical evidence from coastlines, rocks, and fossils the continents were all connected approximately 200 million years ago in a supercontinent called Pangaea.

52) Item Type: Short Answer   Objective: 17-1.2
Level: 1   Tag: None

What do scientists call the theory that describes the motion of the plates?

> The theory describing the movement of the plates is called plate tectonics.

53) Item Type: Short Answer   Objective: 17-1.3
Level: 1   Tag: None

What is subduction and at which type of plate boundary does it occur?

> Subduction occurs at convergent plate boundaries. During subduction, denser plates are forced down into the mantle as less dense crust rides over the top.

54) Item Type: Short Answer   Objective: 17-1.3
Level: 1   Tag: None

What kinds of geologic features form at subduction zones?

> Trenches, volcanoes, and mountains form around subduction zones.

55) Item Type: Short Answer   Objective: 17-1.3
Level: 1   Tag: None

What causes the formation of mountains and volcanoes around subduction zones?

> In the subduction zone, when the denser plate dives into the mantle, the rock reaches its melting point and begins to melt and form magma. This hot, low density magma rises through the crust to the surface to form mountains and volcanoes.

56) Item Type: Short Answer   Objective: 17-1.4
Level: 1   Tag: None

What was the "new" evidence that was discovered that supported the theory of plate tectonics and when was it discovered?

> Bands of rock with alternating magnetic polarities were discovered on either side of the Mid-Atlantic Ridge in the 1960s. As the youngest rock appears near the center of the ridge and the oldest rock appears further away, this suggests that the oceanic plates are moving away from the plate boundary.

57) Item Type: Short Answer   Objective: 17-2.1
Level: I   Tag: None

What is one cause of earthquakes?

Rocks moving past each other at plate boundaries.

58) Item Type: Short Answer   Objective: 17-2.2
Level: I   Tag: None

What is a *seismic wave*?

Energy released as the result of rock movement along a fault.

59) Item Type: Short Answer   Objective: 17-2.2
Level: I   Tag: None

What is the relationship between the focus of an earthquake and its epicenter?

The focus of an earthquake is the location within the lithosphere where seismic energy is released when slippage first occurs along a fault line. The epicenter is the location on Earth's surface directly above the focus.

60) Item Type: Short Answer   Objective: 17-2.3
Level: I   Tag: None

What do values on the Richter scale express?

The Richter scale expresses the relative magnitude of an earthquake, which is a measure of the energy released at the focus of an earthquake.

61) Item Type: Short Answer   Objective: 17-2.3
Level: II   Tag: None

What does the Modified Mercalli scale measure?

The Mercalli scale measures the intensity of an earthquake based on observations of the damage it causes.

62) Item Type: Short Answer   Objective: 17-2.3
Level: I   Tag: None

Which has a higher potential risk, an earthquake with a shallow focus or one with a deep focus, and why?

Shallow focus earthquakes have higher potential risk because more of the energy from the earthquake is transferred to the surface and structures built on the surface. Much of the energy of deep focus earthquakes may be absorbed by the interior of Earth, limiting the amount of energy that is transferred to the surface.

63) Item Type: Short Answer   Objective: 17-2.4
Level: 1   Tag: None

Why are volcanoes common around the edges of the Pacific Ocean?

As the Pacific plate is subducted under surrounding plates, the Pacific plate is forced into the mantle, where the rock melts and rises to the surface, creating volcanoes.

64) Item Type: Short Answer   Objective: 17-2.4
Level: 1   Tag: None

How are volcanoes created at the Mid-Atlantic Ridge?

The Mid-Atlantic Ridge represents a zone of plate divergence. As the plates move away from each other, magma rises up to fill the gap, creating the volcanic mountains that form the ridges around a central rift valley.

65) Item Type: Short Answer   Objective: 17-2.5
Level: 1   Tag: None

Hawaii is one of a group of volcanic islands formed in the middle of a tectonic plate. What type of volcano is most common in Hawaii?

Shield volcanoes.

66) Item Type: Short Answer   Objective: 17-3.1
Level: 1   Tag: None

Which rock type appeared first on Earth? Why?

Igneous rocks came first, because sedimentary and metamorphic rocks are formed from preexisting rocks.

67) Item Type: Short Answer   Objective: 17-3.2
Level: II   Tag: None

What is the difference between extrusive and intrusive igneous rocks?

Intrusive igneous rocks are cooled down slowly beneath Earth's surface, and large crystals form. Extrusive igneous rocks cool down rapidly on Earth's surface, and crystals do not form at all or are very small.

68) Item Type: Short Answer   Objective: 17-3.2
Level: 1   Tag: None

What type of igneous rock contains large mineral crystals? Explain why.

Intrusive igneous rock contains large mineral crystals. The large crystals in intrusive igneous rocks form when magma cools very slowly. Magma that is trapped beneath Earth's surface is insulated by surrounding rocks, and cools and hardens over very long periods.

69) Item Type: Short Answer   Objective: 17-3.4
Level: 1   Tag: None

What is the principle of superposition?

The principle of superposition states that in undisturbed rock layers, the oldest layer of rock will be on the bottom, while the youngest layer will be on the top.

70) Item Type: Short Answer   Objective: 17-3.4
Level: 1   Tag: None

What rock type does the principle of superposition apply to and how is the principle of superposition used to study the history of life on Earth?

The principle of superposition applies to sedimentary rock. It is used to study the sequence of life on Earth. Sedimentary rocks are the only rocks that contain fossils and therefore, a record of ancient life. By applying the principle of superposition, scientists know that fossils in the upper layers are the remains of animals that lived more recently than the animals that were fossilized in lower layers.

71) Item Type: Short Answer   Objective: 17-4.1
Level: 1   Tag: None

Describe the process of frost wedging.

Frost wedging occurs when water seeps into cracks or joints in rock and then freezes. As the water freezes, it expands, causing the crack in the rock to widen. Repetition of this process eventually causes the rock to break apart.

72) Item Type: Short Answer   Objective: 17-4.1
Level: 1   Tag: None

What is chemical weathering?

Chemical weathering is the breakdown of rocks by changing their chemical compositions.

73) Item Type: Short Answer   Objective: 17-4.1
Level: 1   Tag: None

Define erosion.

Erosion is the removal and transportation of weathered and nonweathered materials by running water, wind, waves, ice, underground water, and gravity.

74) Item Type: Short Answer   Objective: 17-4.1
Level: 1   Tag: None

How does water velocity affect the size of particle that running water can transport?

As the water velocity increases, the size of the particles that the water can transport also increases.

75) Item Type: Short Answer   Objective: 17-4.1
Level: II   Tag: None

How does sediment produce more sediment?

When sediment is carried by wind and water, it rubs against large rocks and friction causes additional sediment.

76) Item Type: Short Answer   Objective: 17-4.2
Level: 1   Tag: None

How is carbonic acid responsible for the formation of some caves?

When carbon dioxide dissolves in water, it produces an acidic solution of carbonic acid. When this weak acid combines with limestone, the calcite in the limestone dissolves away, leaving holes. As more calcite is dissolved the holes may widen to produce caves.

77) Item Type: Short Answer   Objective: 17-4.3
Level: 1   Tag: None

Why is acid rain a major biological concern?

Acid rain damages both living and nonliving things. Acid rain has been implicated in the destruction of pine trees, particularly in Germany.

78) Item Type: Short Answer   Objective: 17-4.3
Level: 1   Tag: None

What steps have power plants taken to reduce the amount of sulfur oxides released into the air?

They have installed scrubbers that remove the sulfur oxide gases.

79) Item Type: Essay   Objective: 17-1.3
Level: II   Tag: None

The Himalayas are a mountain range in India that continues to increase in both width and height. Describe the type of plate boundary found in this region and explain the reason behind the formation of the mountain range.

The formation of the Himalayas is caused by the tectonic collision in a zone of convergence between the plate containing Asia and the plate containing India. The rocks in the region of the collision are made up of relatively low density continental crust. Because of their relatively low density, as India continues to push into Asia, the rocks continue to pile up, causing the mountains in the region to increase in height.

80) Item Type: Essay   Objective: 17-2.2
Level: II   Tag: None

How do seismograms recorded during earthquakes help scientists learn about the composition of Earth?

Seismograms give information about the path of seismic waves and the speed of seismic waves. The speed of seismic waves depends on the density of the material the seismic wave is travelling in. We know, for example, that the core of Earth is liquid, because S waves do not travel through the center of Earth.

81) Item Type: Essay   Objective: 17-2.3
Level: II   Tag: None

How does a seismograph work?

A stationary pendulum hangs from a support fastened to Earth. The pendulum has a pen on its tip. Below the pendulum is a rotating drum covered by paper. When the ground shakes, the pendulum remains relatively still while the base of the seismograph and the drum moves with Earth. The stationary pen creates a zigzag line on the paper-covered drum as the drum moves in response to the shaking Earth.

82) Item Type: Essay   Objective: 17-3.2
Level: III   Tag: None

In an earthquake-prone area, which earth material—igneous rock or sedimentary rock—would be better for constructing buildings? Explain your answer.

The rock with the most solid structure will be the best choice for construction in an earthquake-prone area. Because sedimentary rock is formed as the result of compaction and cementation of preexisting rock particles, sedimentary rock isn't as rigid and doesn't have the same strength as igneous rock. As magma cools and solidifies, the minerals crystallize, forming igneous rock. Igneous rock forms a stronger, more stable base on which to build. The mineral cement that holds rock particles together in sedimentary rock can be shaken loose and broken in an earthquake.

83) Item Type: Essay   Objective: 17-4.3
     Level: III   Tag: None

Why is acid rain a social and political problem?

Acid rain is caused by human activity that pollutes the enviornment. The burning of fossil fuels releases sulfur oxides into the air. When combined with water in the air the sulfer oxides produce acids such as sulfuric acid. This combines with naturally occurring acids to cause acid rain. Environmental protection laws are passed to reduce the amount of air pollution.

1) Tag Name: Rock cycle

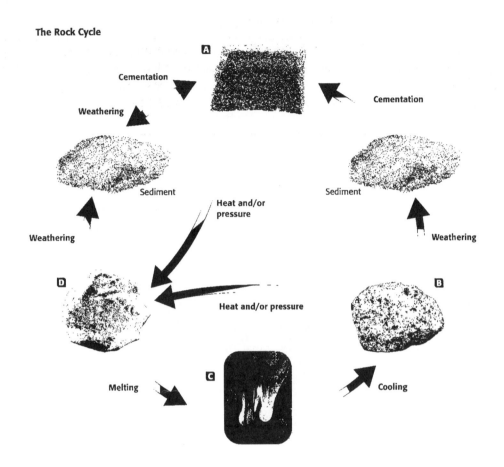

2)   Tag Name: valley

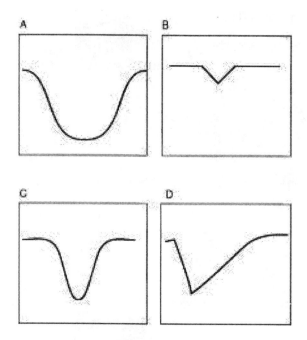

Chapter 18

1) Item Type: Multiple Choice   Objective: 18-1.1
   Level: I   Tag: None

The coldest layer of Earth's atmosphere is the

   a) troposphere.   b) stratosphere.

   c) mesosphere.   d) thermosphere.

   c

2) Item Type: Multiple Choice   Objective: 18-1.1
   Level: I   Tag: None

Almost all weather occurs in the

   a) troposphere.   b) stratosphere.

   c) mesosphere.   d) thermosphere.

   a

3) Item Type: Multiple Choice   Objective: 18-1.1
   Level: I   Tag: None

Of all the atmospheric layers, the troposphere has the

   a) highest temperatures.   b) lowest temperatures.

   c) highest density.   d) lowest density.

   c

4) Item Type: Multiple Choice   Objective: 18-1.1
   Level: I   Tag: None

The boundary between the troposphere and stratosphere is called the

   a) thermopause.   b) mesopause.

   c) stratopause.   d) tropopause.

   d

5) Item Type: Multiple Choice   Objective: 18-1.1
   Level: I   Tag: None

As distance from Earth's surface increases, the temperature of the stratosphere

   a) decreases.   b) increases.

   c) remains the same.   d) none of the above

   b

Chapter 18

6) Item Type: Multiple Choice   Objective: 18-1.1
   Level: I   Tag: None

The ozone layer is located in the

        a) troposphere.   b) stratosphere.

        c) mesosphere.   d) thermosphere.

b

7) Item Type: Multiple Choice   Objective: 18-1.1
   Level: I   Tag: None

The region where electrically charged ions are formed as a result of the absorption of solar energy is called the

        a) troposphere.   b) lithosphere.

        c) ionosphere.   d) exosphere.

c

8) Item Type: Multiple Choice   Objective: 18-1.2
   Level: I   Tag: None

Which of the following gases was not believed to be present on Earth at the time of its formation 4.4 billion years ago?

        a) oxygen   b) nitrogen

        c) water   d) methane

a

9) Item Type: Multiple Choice   Objective: 18-1.2
   Level: I   Tag: None

Oxygen was introduced into the atmosphere as a byproduct of

        a) respiration.   b) photosynthesis.

        c) dehydration.   d) osmosis.

b

10) Item Type: Multiple Choice　　　Objective: 18-1.3
　　Level: I　　　　　　　　　　Tag: None

In the oxygen—carbon dioxide cycle,

a) animals produce oxygen used by plants for photosynthesis.

b) animals produce oxygen used by plants for respiration.

c) animals produce carbon dioxide used by plants for photosynthesis.

d) animals produce carbon dioxide used by plants for respiration.

c

11) Item Type: Multiple Choice　　　Objective: 18-1.3
　　Level: I　　　　　　　　　　Tag: None

A waste product of respiration in animals that is used by plants to carry out photosynthesis is

a) carbon dioxide.

b) carbon monoxide.

c) calcium carbonate.

d) sodium bicarbonate.

a

12) Item Type: Multiple Choice　　　Objective: 18-1.4
　　Level: I　　　　　　　　　　Tag: None

Ozone molecules are destroyed by

a) carbon dioxide molecules.

b) chlorofluorocarbons.

c) deoxyribonucleic acids.

d) ultraviolet radiation.

b

13) Item Type: Multiple Choice　　　Objective: 18-1.4
　　Level: I　　　　　　　　　　Tag: None

Greenhouse gases are added to the atmosphere through

a) forest fires.

b) photosynthesis.

c) radiation.

d) absorption.

a

14) Item Type: Multiple Choice   Objective: 18-1.4
    Level: I   Tag: None

In the last 100 years, which of the following have added excess carbon dioxide to the atmosphere?

    a) power plants   b) machinery

    c) cars   d) all of the above

d

15) Item Type: Multiple Choice   Objective: 18-2.1
    Level: I   Tag: None

On Earth, water exists as

    a) a solid.   b) a liquid.

    c) a gas.   d) all of the above

d

16) Item Type: Multiple Choice   Objective: 18-2.1
    Level: I   Tag: None

The only atmospheric layer containing measurable amounts of water is the

    a) stratosphere.   b) troposphere.

    c) mesophere.   d) thermosphere.

b

17) Item Type: Multiple Choice   Objective: 18-2.1
    Level: I   Tag: None

With the input of solar energy, water changes from a liquid to a gas during the process of

    a) condensation.   b) precipitation.

    c) evaporation.   d) neutralization.

c

18) Item Type: Multiple Choice   Objective: 18-2.1
    Level: I   Tag: None

Plants contribute large volumes of atmospheric water vapor to the air through the process of

    a) transpiration.   b) condensation.

    c) evaporation.   d) respiration.

a

19) Item Type: Multiple Choice   Objective: 18-2.2
    Level: I   Tag: None

As temperature increases, the possible total humidity

a) increases.   b) decreases.

c) increases and then   d) remains the same.
decreases.

a

20) Item Type: Multiple Choice   Objective: 18-2.2
    Level: I   Tag: None

Warm, moist air will have

a) high humidity and low dew   b) low humidity and high
point.   dew point.

c) high humidity and high dew   d) low humidity and low dew
point.   point.

c

21) Item Type: Multiple Choice   Objective: 18-2.3
    Level: I   Tag: None

The clouds that occur at the highest altitude are usually

a) cirrus.   b) stratus.

c) cumulus.   d) nimbus.

a

22) Item Type: Multiple Choice   Objective: 18-2.3
    Level: I   Tag: None

Sheet-shaped clouds are called

a) cirrus.   b) stratus.

c) cumulus.   d) nimbus.

b

23) Item Type: Multiple Choice   Objective: 18-2.3
    Level: II   Tag: None

Condensation and the formation of cumulus clouds begins as the rising air reaches its

a) dew point.   b) maximum altitude.

c) minimum altitude.   d) evaporation point.

a

24) Item Type: Multiple Choice   Objective: 18-2.3
    Level: I   Tag: None

A cloud type that usually produces precipitation is a(n)

          a) cirrostratus.   b) altostratus.

          c) altocumulus.   d) nimbostratus.

d

25) Item Type: Multiple Choice   Objective: 18-2.4
    Level: II   Tag: None

In a high-pressure system,

a) air molecules are far apart and pressing on Earth's surface.

b) air molecules are far apart and rising away from Earth's surface.

c) air molecules are close together and pressing on Earth's surface.

d) air molecules are close together and rising away from Earth's surface.

c

26) Item Type: Multiple Choice   Objective: 18-2.4
    Level: I   Tag: None

Air becomes wind as it flows from

a) low pressure to low pressure.

b) high pressure to high pressure.

c) low pressure to high pressure.

d) high pressure to low pressure.

d

27) Item Type: Multiple Choice   Objective: 18-2.4
    Level: I   Tag: None

The direction in which the wind moves is influenced by

          a) the pressure gradient.   b) Earth's rotation.

          c) a only   d) both a and b

d

28) Item Type: Multiple Choice   Objective: 18-2.4
Level: I   Tag: None

Due to the Coriolis effect, winds in the Northern Hemisphere

       a) curve to the north.   b) curve clockwise.

       c) curve to the south.   d) curve counterclockwise.

b

29) Item Type: Multiple Choice   Objective: 18-2.4
Level: I   Tag: None

Warm air rises because of its

       a) low density.   b) high density.

       c) lack of density.   d) lack of pressure.

a

30) Item Type: Multiple Choice   Objective: 18-2.4
Level: I   Tag: None

The general geographic location of a large low-pressure system is

       a) the North Pole.   b) the South Pole.

       c) the tropics.   d) 30 degrees latitude.

c

31) Item Type: Multiple Choice   Objective: 18-3.1
Level: I   Tag: None

The region where warm and cold air masses meet is called a

       a) pocket.   b) cloud.

       c) front.   d) nimbus.

c

32) Item Type: Multiple Choice   Objective: 18-3.1
Level: I   Tag: None

The leading edge of a cold air mass that overtakes a region formally occupied by a warm air mass is called a

       a) warm front.   b) cold front.

       c) stationary front.   d) occluded front.

b

Chapter 18

33) Item Type: Multiple Choice   Objective: 18-3.1
    Level: I   Tag: None

High winds and strong thunderstorms are characteristic of an approaching strong

      a) warm front.   b) cold front.

      c) stationary front.   d) occluded front.

b

34) Item Type: Multiple Choice   Objective: 18-3.2
    Level: I   Tag: None

As the electrical energy of lightning is discharged into the air,

      a) the air cools and condenses rapidly.   b) the air heats and condenses rapidly.

      c) the air cools and expands rapidly.   d) the air heats and expands rapidly.

d

35) Item Type: Multiple Choice   Objective: 18-3.2
    Level: I   Tag: None

Tornadoes commonly occur in which of the following regions of the United States?

      a) Midwest   b) Northwest

      c) Northeast   d) Southeast

a

36) Item Type: Multiple Choice   Objective: 18-3.2
    Level: I   Tag: None

The energy that powers a hurricane is derived from

      a) a stationary front.   b) condensation of water vapor.

      c) funnel clouds.   d) sublimation of water.

b

Chapter 18

37) Item Type: Multiple Choice   Objective: 18-3.3
    Level: I   Tag: None

Weather variables such as wind speed, cloud cover, and precipitation are indicated on weather maps by

a) numbers.   b) colors.

c) symbols.   d) none of the above

c

38) Item Type: Multiple Choice   Objective: 18-3.3
    Level: I   Tag: None

On a weather map, winds blow slightly across isobars

a) toward high-pressure   b) away from low-pressure
centers.   centers.

c) against the pressure   d) toward low-pressure
gradient.   centers.

d

39) Item Type: Multiple Choice   Objective: 18-3.4
    Level: I   Tag: None

Unlike climate, weather

a) changes from day to day.   b) is the average weather of a
                                region.

c) is the weather conditions   d) both b and c
over many years.

a

40) Item Type: Multiple Choice   Objective: 18-3.5
    Level: II   Tag: None

The climate of a region or location is affected by

a) latitude.   b) elevation.

c) season.   d) all of the above

d

41) Item Type: Multiple Choice   Objective: 18-3.5
      Level: II   Tag: None

The climate of a region is defined by which two variables?

           a) temperature and elevation   b) elevation and topography

           c) moisture and topography   d) temperature and moisture

d

42) Item Type: Multiple Choice   Objective: 18-3.5
      Level: I   Tag: None

Historically, global climate

           a) has always been the same.   b) has varied slightly over
                                              time.

           c) has varied greatly over time.   d) none of the above

c

43) Item Type: Short Answer   Objective: 18-1.1
      Level: I   Tag: None

What physical characteristic of the atmosphere changes as altitude increases?

Temperature is a distinguishing characteristic that changes from atmospheric layer to atmospheric layer.

44) Item Type: Short Answer   Objective: 18-1.1
      Level: I   Tag: None

What are the two main gases in the atmosphere?

The two main gases in the atmosphere are nitrogen and oxygen.

45) Item Type: Short Answer   Objective: 18-1.1
      Level: I   Tag: atmosphere

How does the temperature of the troposphere change as altitude increases?

The troposphere gets cooler with increasing altitude.

46) Item Type: Short Answer   Objective: 18-1.1
      Level: I   Tag: None

What produces a temperature inversion?

A temperature inversion is produced when cool air is trapped by warm air concentrating pollutants at ground level.

47) Item Type: Short Answer   Objective: 18-1.1
    Level: 1   Tag: None

Where is the ozone layer located and what does it do?

The ozone layer is located within the stratosphere. This layer acts like a blanket that absorbs incoming solar radiation.

48) Item Type: Short Answer   Objective: 18-1.2
    Level: 1   Tag: None

Where do scientists believe the first gases that created the atmosphere came from?

During the process of outgassing, volcanic eruptions emitted the gases that founded the primitive atmosphere.

49) Item Type: Short Answer   Objective: 18-1.2
    Level: 1   Tag: None

What were the first organisms to add oxygen to the atmosphere?

Photosynthetic bacteria were the first organisms to add oxygen to the atmosphere.

50) Item Type: Short Answer   Objective: 18-1.2
    Level: 1   Tag: None

How long has the oxygen concentration of the atmosphere been at its current level?

Oxygen reached concentration levels similar to the concentration of oxygen in today's atmosphere about 350 million years ago.

51) Item Type: Short Answer   Objective: 18-1.3
    Level: 1   Tag: None

How do plants and animals rely on each other to maintain the atmospheric oxygen and carbon dioxide content?

Carbon dioxide-producing animals balance oxygen producing plants creating the carbon dioxide-oxygen cycle that keeps the gases from these sources in equilibrium.

52) Item Type: Short Answer   Objective: 18-1.4
    Level: 1   Tag: None

What is the molecular formula of ozone?

The molecular formula of ozone is O_3.

53) Item Type: Short Answer   Objective: 18-1.4
    Level: 1   Tag: None

What causes low ozone concentrations in the atmosphere?

Low ozone concentrations are caused in part by chlorofluorocarbons, or CFCs.

54) Item Type: Short Answer   Objective: 18-1.4
    Level: 1   Tag: None

What is meant by the "greenhouse effect"?

The greenhouse effect is caused by Earth's radiated heat that is absorbed by CO_2 and H_2O in the atmosphere, prohibiting the heat from radiating back out into space.

55) Item Type: Short Answer   Objective: 18-1.4
    Level: 1   Tag: None

What is the relationship between the greenhouse effect and global warming?

An increase in global temperatures as a result of the greenhouse effect is called global warming. As more and more heat becomes trapped within our atmosphere, the overall temperature of Earth is expected to increase.

56) Item Type: Short Answer   Objective: 18-2.1
    Level: II   Tag: None

What drives the water cycle?

The water cycle is the continuous phase changing of water as the result of energy processes. Incoming solar radiation provides the energy necessary to change liquid water into water vapor. As water vapor cools and condenses, forming liquid water from water vapor, energy is released.

57) Item Type: Short Answer   Objective: 18-2.1
    Level: 1   Tag: None

What is liquid water converted to during evaporation?

Water in its gaseous form is called water vapor.

58) Item Type: Short Answer   Objective: 18-2.1
    Level: 1   Tag: None

What is the original source of energy that drives the water cycle?

Solar energy drives the water cycle.

59) Item Type: Short Answer   Objective: 18-2.2
    Level: 1   Tag: None

Do water vapor molecules move more quickly at higher temperatures or at lower temperatures?

At warm temperatures, water vapor molecules move more quickly than at cooler temperatures.

60) Item Type: Short Answer   Objective: 18-2.2
       Level: I   Tag: None

What is relative humidity?

The amount of water that the air holds when compared to how much water *could* be in the air referred to as relative humidity.

61) Item Type: Short Answer   Objective: 18-2.2
       Level: I   Tag: None

When is a volume of air saturated?

Air is saturated when it has a relative humidity of 100 percent. When the air is saturated, the amount of water vapor that could be in the air is equal to the amount of water vapor contained in the air. The addition of any more water vapor to the air would cause excess water vapor to condense forming water droplets.

62) Item Type: Short Answer   Objective: 18-2.2
       Level: II   Tag: None

What is the relationship between air temperature and its density?

As the temperature of air decreases, the density of air increases.

63) Item Type: Short Answer   Objective: 18-2.3
       Level: I   Tag: None

List the three main types of clouds.

The three main types of clouds are cirrus, stratus, and cumulus.

64) Item Type: Short Answer   Objective: 18-2.3
       Level: I   Tag: None

What are two general characteristics that define each cloud type?

Each cloud type forms at a relatively specific altitude and has a characteristic shape.

65) Item Type: Short Answer   Objective: 18-2.3
       Level: I   Tag: None

Which cloud type is associated with thunderstorms?

Cumulonimbus clouds often produce thunderstorms.

66) Item Type: Short Answer   Objective: 18-2.4
       Level: I   Tag: None

Define air pressure.

The pressure due to the weight of the atmosphere is called air pressure.

Chapter 18

67) Item Type: Short Answer   Objective: 18-2.4
Level: 1   Tag: None

How is air pressure measured?

A barometer is an instrument used to measure air pressure.

68) Item Type: Short Answer   Objective: 18-2.4
Level: 1   Tag: None

What causes a pressure gradient?

The difference in atmospheric pressures in different geographic locations causes a pressure gradient.

69) Item Type: Short Answer   Objective: 18-2.4
Level: II   Tag: None

When presented with a geographic region with high pressure in the west and a low-pressure system in the east, in what direction will the wind blow? Support your answer.

Air will always flow from an area of high pressure to an area of low pressure. Because the low pressure is in the east and the high pressure is in the west, the wind will blow out of the west toward the east.

70) Item Type: Short Answer   Objective: 18-2.4
Level: 1   Tag: None

What is wind and what causes it?

The movement of air along a pressure gradient is called wind.

71) Item Type: Short Answer   Objective: 18-2.4
Level: II   Tag: None

What causes the Coriolis effect?

Earth's rotation causes the deflection of wind to the right or left of its direct path.

72) Item Type: Short Answer   Objective: 18-2.4
Level: II   Tag: None

What are global wind belts and what causes them?

Global wind belts are general geographic regions characterized by winds that blow predominantly from a single direction. Global wind belts are established by differences in air pressure over the surface of Earth. Consistent warm temperatures in the tropics create a large region of rising warm, moist air setting up a low-pressure system. As the air rises, more air is pulled into the equatorial region, forming a circulation cell.

73) Item Type: Short Answer   Objective: 18-3.1
     Level: 1   Tag: None

What changes can be expected with the passage of a weather front?

When a front moves through an area, the result is usually precipitation and a change in wind direction and temperature.

74) Item Type: Short Answer   Objective: 18-3.1
     Level: 1   Tag: None

What are the general atmospheric conditions behind a cold front?

The air behind a cold front is cool and dry.

75) Item Type: Short Answer   Objective: 18-3.1
     Level: 1   Tag: None

What are the general atmospheric conditions behind a warm front?

The air behind a warm front is warm and moist.

76) Item Type: Short Answer   Objective: 18-3.1
     Level: 1   Tag: None

What happens to a warm air mass as it moves into an area occupied by a cold air mass?

In a warm front, a warm air mass moves above a slower cold air mass. This cool air mass cools the warm air, causing the formation of clouds and precipitation.

77) Item Type: Short Answer   Objective: 18-3.1
     Level: 1   Tag: None

How can you tell a cold front is approaching?

Cumulonimbus clouds characterize an advancing cold front.

78) Item Type: Short Answer   Objective: 18-3.1
     Level: 1   Tag: None

Does a front always mean one air mass will be displaced by another? When is there no displacement?

A stationary front occurs when two air masses meet but neither is displaced.

79) Item Type: Short Answer   Objective: 18-3.2
     Level: 1   Tag: None

What is a tornado?

Tornadoes are high-speed, rotating winds that extend downward from thunderclouds.

Chapter 18

80) Item Type: Short Answer   Objective: 18-3.2
    Level: I   Tag: None

What are the beginnings of a tornado called?

Funnel clouds. A funnel cloud is a tapered column of water droplets that reaches down from storm clouds.

81) Item Type: Short Answer   Objective: 18-3.2
    Level: I   Tag: None

When does a tropical storm become a hurricane?

Wind speeds must meet or exceed 118 km/h in order for a storm to be classified as a hurricane.

82) Item Type: Short Answer   Objective: 18-3.3
    Level: I   Tag: None

What are isobars?

On a weather map, isobars are lines that connect points of equal barometric pressure.

83) Item Type: Short Answer   Objective: 18-3.3
    Level: II   Tag: None

What do isobars indicate on a weather map?

Isobars indicate points of equal barometric pressure.

84) Item Type: Short Answer   Objective: 18-3.4
    Level: I   Tag: None

How are climate and weather related?

The average weather of a region describes that region's climate.

85) Item Type: Short Answer   Objective: 18-3.5
    Level: I   Tag: None

Earth's location within its orbit is not solely responsible for the seasons. What is a contributing factor to the reason for the seasons?

Earth's tilt affects the seasons.

86) Item Type: Short Answer   Objective: 18-3.5
    Level: I   Tag: None

In the northern hemisphere, the warmest months of the year are June, July, and August. During what season is Earth closest to the sun?

Earth is closest to the sun during the winter season in the Northern Hemisphere.

87) Item Type: Short Answer   Objective: 18-3.5
Level: I   Tag: None

Proximity to water is one topographic feature that can and often does moderate the climate of a region. What is another topographic feature that affects a region's climate?

> Mountains are topographic features that have a profound effect on the climate of a region.

88) Item Type: Essay   Objective: 18-1.1
Level: II   Tag: atmosphere

List the layers of the atmosphere in order, starting with the one closest to Earth, and describe how temperature changes as altitude increases.

> The atmospheric layer closest to Earth is the troposphere. Temperature decreases as distance above the surface of Earth increases. Temperature remains the same briefly during the transition from the troposphere to the next atmospheric layer, the stratosphere. Increasing altitude through the stratosphere results in an increase in temperature. There is a dramatic change in rate that results in a rapid increase toward the upper portion of this layer. As altitude continues to increase, there is a dramatic decrease in temperature at the boundary between the stratosphere and the mesosphere. Temperature decreases at a rapid and constant rate throughout the mesospheric layer as altitude continues to increase. The boundary between the mesosphere and thermosphere marks a rapid return to increasing temperatures, which continues to the outer limits of the atmosphere.

89) Item Type: Essay   Objective: 18-2.1
Level: II   Tag: None

Describe the three phases of the water cycle.

> Energy from the sun causes liquid water to escape into the atmosphere through evaporation forming water vapor. As temperature decreases with increasing altitude, the air cools and condenses, forming water droplets of liquid water. With the addition of more water vapor and under the right atmospheric conditions, droplets become larger, eventually becoming too heavy to remain suspended in the air, and they fall as precipitation.

90) Item Type: Essay   Objective: 18-2.4
Level: II   Tag: None

What is meant by the term "Westerlies" and how do they affect meteorological attempts to predict the weather?

> Westerlies is a term applied to the general west-to-east flow of global winds between 30 degrees and 60 degrees north and south of the equator. Within this wind belt, winds blow weather systems almost consistently from west to east. Therefore, when predicting the weather for a specific location, in addition to other variables, meteorologists review the weather conditions of points west of their location.

Chapter 18

91) Item Type: Essay   Objective: 18-3.2
    Level: II   Tag: None

Describe the formation of a tornado.

> Tornadoes are high-speed rotating winds that extend downward from thunderclouds.
> Tornadoes form along the front between air masses with distinctly different temperature
> and moisture characteristics on either side of the front. Cold, dry air is very dense and
> sinks. As cold dry air encounters warm, moist, rising air from the south, the warm air is
> forced to rise faster. As the warm air rises, it may begin to spin, potentially becoming a
> strong, rotating thunderstorm that can spawn a tornado.

92) Item Type: Essay   Objective: 18-1.1
    Level: III   Tag: None

The cabins of airplanes are pressurized and the temperature is internally controlled. Why
are all planes constructed this way and what would happen if these systems failed?

> As an airplane increases in altitude through the troposphere, air temperature and pressure
> decrease. Cabin pressure and temperature are controlled for the safety and comfort of the
> people on board. Prolonged loss of cabin pressure and temperature would physically affect
> the passengers and crew and potentially cause the plane to crash.

93) Item Type: Essay   Objective: 18-1.4
    Level: III   Tag: None

You are well acquainted with the negative effects of the greenhouse effect, but the fact
remains that without it, Earth would be a very different place. How would our world be
different if there were no such thing as the greenhouse effect?

> Earth would be a much colder place—possibly too cold for life to exist and certainly too
> cold for humans.

1)   Tag Name: atmosphere

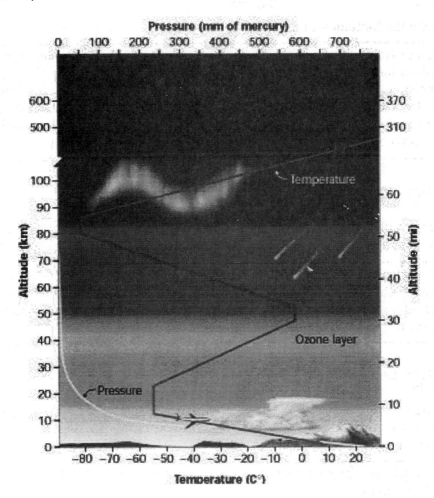

1)   Item Type: Multiple Choice   Objective: 19-1.1
      Level: I   Tag: None

Which of the following statements about ecosystems is not true?

a) Ecosystems include living   b) Temperature and climate
and nonliving things.   are not part of an ecosystem.

c) An ecosystem can be as   d) Sunlight, air, and water can
small as a rain puddle.   be parts of an ecosystem.

b

2)   Item Type: Multiple Choice   Objective: 19-1.1
      Level: I   Tag: None

Which of the following animals are adapted to cold, wet places?

a) polar bears   b) lions

c) elephants   d) mosquitoes

a

3)   Item Type: Multiple Choice   Objective: 19-1.1
      Level: I   Tag: None

Groups of plants and animals that are adapted to similar conditions form a(n)

a) population.   b) ecosystem.

c) community.   d) organism.

c

4)   Item Type: Multiple Choice   Objective: 19-1.2
      Level: I   Tag: None

An ecosystem is balanced when

a) energy does not enter or   b) there are an equal number
leave the ecosystem.   of plants and animals.

c) there is plenty of rain.   d) there are enough resources
                                 for every living thing.

d

5) Item Type: Multiple Choice   Objective: 19-1.2
    Level: II   Tag: None

In a balanced ecosystem with predators and prey, if the number of prey decreases

    a) the number of predators   b) new predators will move
    will decrease.   into the area.

    c) there will be no change in   d) the number of prey will
    the ecosystem.   eventually increase.

a

6) Item Type: Multiple Choice   Objective: 19-1.3
    Level: II   Tag: None

A forest destroyed by a fire will gradually become a complex ecosystem with a wide
variety of plants and animals in a process called

    a) regeneration.   b) evolution.

    c) succession.   d) development.

c

7) Item Type: Multiple Choice   Objective: 19-1.3
    Level: II   Tag: None

An example of a short-term ecological change is

    a) a volcanic eruption.   b) a large and devastating forest fire.

    c) change in seasons.   d) global temperature change.

c

8) Item Type: Multiple Choice   Objective: 19-1.3
    Level: II   Tag: None

Which of the following statements about the ice ages is true?

    a) An ice age will never   b) The causes of ice ages are
    come again.   well known.

    c) During the ice ages, icy   d) There were no living
    glaciers covered much of the   organisms during the ice ages.
    continents.

c

Chapter 19

9) Item Type: Multiple Choice   Objective: 19-1.4
   Level: II   Tag: None

The following is not a benefit of building a dam.

a) flood control   b) irrigation

c) generating hydroelectric   d) increased need for
power   fertilizers

d

10) Item Type: Multiple Choice   Objective: 19-2.2
    Level: I   Tag: None

Nonrenewable resources are

a) resources that are used   b) very expensive resources.
faster than they can be
replaced.

c) energy from the sun.   d) rare earth elements.

a

11) Item Type: Multiple Choice   Objective: 19-2.2
    Level: I   Tag: None

Which of the following is not a renewable resource?

a) sunlight   b) wind

c) water   d) natural gas

d

12) Item Type: Multiple Choice   Objective: 19-2.3
    Level: I   Tag: None

Solar cells

a) photograph sunspots.   b) convert sunlight into
                                  electricity.

c) convert sunlight and carbon   d) convert electricity into solar
dioxide into sugars.   energy.

b

13) Item Type: Multiple Choice   Objective: 19-2.1
Level: I   Tag: None

Fossil fuels include

        a) coal and oil.   b) wood and charcoal.

        c) coal, natural gas, and oil.   d) hydrogen, oxygen, and
                                                 acetylene.

c

14) Item Type: Multiple Choice   Objective: 19-2.2
Level: II   Tag: None

The percent of the world's energy sources that are fossil fuels is

        a) 39%.   b) 44%.

        c) 14%.   d) 86%.

d

15) Item Type: Multiple Choice   Objective: 19-2.1
Level: I   Tag: None

Which of the following is not considered an alternative source of energy?

        a) energy from the sun   b) wind and water energy

        c) electricity   d) natural gas

d

16) Item Type: Multiple Choice   Objective: 19-2.2
Level: II   Tag: None

Which of the following statements about wind energy is not true?

        a) Wind energy is a   b) Wind energy is used to sail
        nonrenewable energy resource.   ships.

        c) Wind energy is not reliable.   d) Windmills are currently
                                             being used to provide energy.

a

Chapter 19

17) Item Type: Multiple Choice   Objective: 19-2.2
    Level: II   Tag: None

Which of the following statements about geothermal energy is not true?

a) It is not a practical source of energy.

b) It is an important source of energy in volcanically active areas.

c) It works best when the magma pool is near the surface of Earth.

d) It is a renewable source of energy.

a

18) Item Type: Multiple Choice   Objective: 19-2.1
    Level: II   Tag: None

Fossil fuels come from

a) living plants and animals.

b) atomic reactions.

c) soil.

d) remains of dead organisms.

d

19) Item Type: Multiple Choice   Objective: 19-2.3
    Level: II   Tag: None

Dams are built on fast-moving rivers to

a) make a large lake for recreation.

b) improve irrigation.

c) create a large holding place for water.

d) protect wildlife.

c

20) Item Type: Multiple Choice   Objective: 19-2.1
    Level: II   Tag: None

Which of the following is not a fossil fuel?

a) oil

b) natural gas

c) coal

d) hydrogen

d

21) Item Type: Multiple Choice   Objective: 19-3.1
     Level: II   Tag: None

Which of the following equations describes the reaction for burning methane?

      a) $2\ CH_4 \rightarrow C_2H_6 + H_2$ b) $CH_4 + 2O_2 \rightarrow CO_2 + 2H_2O$

      c) $C + 2H_2 \rightarrow CH_4$ d) $6\ CH_4 + 6O_2 \rightarrow C_6H_{12}O_6 + 6H_2O$

b

22) Item Type: Multiple Choice   Objective: 19-3.1
     Level: II   Tag: None

Carbon dioxide is called a greenhouse gas because

      a) it is used inside of   b) plants need carbon dioxide
      greenhouses.   to grow.

      c) it helps keep the temperature   d) it is produced when wood
      of our planet balanced.   or fossil fuels are burned.

c

23) Item Type: Multiple Choice   Objective: 19-3.1
     Level: II   Tag: None

In the past 100 years the average temperature in the United States has increased by

      a) an amount too small to measure.   b) 2°C.

      c) 10°C.   d) 20°C.

b

24) Item Type: Multiple Choice   Objective: 19-3.1
     Level: II   Tag: None

Bacteria and algae in a pond sometimes kill fish and other aquatic wildlife because they

      a) crowd out other forms of   b) infect other organisms and
      life.   cause diseases.

      c) secrete a poisonous   d) use up most of the oxygen
      substance.   in the water.

d

25) Item Type: Multiple Choice   Objective: 19-3.2
    Level: II   Tag: None

Which of the following is not a pollutant caused by burning fossil fuels?

　　　　　　　a) carbon monoxide　　　　　　b) nitrate ions

　　　　　　　c) nitrogen oxides　　　　　　d) volatile organic compounds

b

26) Item Type: Multiple Choice   Objective: 19-3.3
    Level: II   Tag: None

When nitrogen oxide compounds in car exhaust react with sunlight the result is

　　　　　　　a) acid rain.　　　　　　　　b) photochemical smog.

　　　　　　　c) nitrogen fixing.　　　　　　d) the greenhouse effect.

b

27) Item Type: Multiple Choice   Objective: 19-3.3
    Level: II   Tag: None

DDT was banned from use as a pesticide in the United States because

　　　　a) it caused the eggs of　　　　b) it was washed by rain into
　　　　fish-eating birds to become　　　streams, rivers, lakes, and
　　　　thin and fragile.　　　　　　　ponds.

　　　　c) it was ingested by fish and　d) all of the above
　　　　other aquatic animals.

d

28) Item Type: Multiple Choice   Objective: 19-3.3
    Level: II   Tag: None

Which of the following is not an air pollutant?

　　　　　　　a) carbon monoxide　　　　　b) carbon dioxide

　　　　　　　c) sulfur dioxide　　　　　　d) particulate matter

b

Chapter 19

29) Item Type: Multiple Choice   Objective: 19-3.3
    Level: II   Tag: Figure 19-23

What is the largest source of particulate matter pollution?

a) transportation   b) fuel burning (not including
                                     transportation)

c) industrial processes   d) construction, agriculture, and
                                     unpaved roads

d

30) Item Type: Multiple Choice   Objective: 19-3.3
    Level: II   Tag: None

What is the largest source of sulfur dioxide air pollution?

a) transportation   b) the greenhouse effect

c) burning fossil fuels in   d) construction, agriculture, and
   vehicles, power stations, and   unpaved roads
   factories

c

31) Item Type: Multiple Choice   Objective: 19-3.3
    Level: II   Tag: None

The burning of fossil fuels produces

a) land pollution.   b) air pollution only.

c) acid rain only.   d) acid rain and air pollution.

d

32) Item Type: Multiple Choice   Objective: 19-3.4
    Level: II   Tag: None

Nonpolluting sources of energy include

a) coal, oil, and natural gas.   b) nuclear energy.

c) alcohol and acetylene.   d) wind, solar, and hydroelectric power.

d

33) Item Type: True-False   Objective: 19-1.1
    Level: II   Tag: None

An organism can be a member of only one community at a time.

F

34) Item Type: Fill-in-the-Blank   Objective: 19-1.1
     Level: I   Tag: None

Groups of animals and plants that are adapted to similar conditions form a

_____.

| community |

35) Item Type: Fill-in-the-Blank   Objective: 19-1.1
     Level: I   Tag: None

All of the living and nonliving elements in a particular place is called a(n)

_____.

| ecosystem |

36) Item Type: True-False   Objective: 19-1.1
     Level: I   Tag: None

An ecosystem must cover a large area and include many different species.

| F |

37) Item Type: Fill-in-the-Blank   Objective: 19-1.2
     Level: II   Tag: None

There can be several _____ in an ecosystem.

| communities |

38) Item Type: Fill-in-the-Blank   Objective: 19-1.2
     Level: II   Tag: None

When there are enough resources for every living thing in an ecosystem, the ecosystem is

| balanced |

39) Item Type: True-False   Objective: 19-1.2
     Level: II   Tag: None

When an ecosystem is balanced, the population sizes of the different species do not change relative to one another.

| T |

40) Item Type: True-False   Objective: 19-1.3
     Level: I   Tag: None

Nonnative plants and animals pose no danger to an ecosystem.

| F |

41) Item Type: Fill-in-the-Blank   Objective: 19-1.4
     Level: I   Tag: None

_____ is the energy of moving water converted to electricity.

Hydroelectric power

42) Item Type: Fill-in-the-Blank   Objective: 19-2.1
     Level: I   Tag: None

Fuels formed from the remains of ancient plant and animal life are called _____ .

fossil fuels

43) Item Type: True-False   Objective: 19-2.2
     Level: II   Tag: None

A disadvantage of nuclear energy from nuclear fission is that it produces large amounts of radioactive waste.

T

44) Item Type: True-False   Objective: 19-2.2
     Level: II   Tag: None

Nuclear fusion is currently a practical alternative source of energy.

F

45) Item Type: Fill-in-the-Blank   Objective: 19-2.3
     Level: I   Tag: None

When fossil fuels are burned they form water and _____ and release energy.

carbon dioxide

46) Item Type: Fill-in-the-Blank   Objective: 19-2.2
     Level: I   Tag: None

Resources that can be continually replaced are called _____ .

renewable resources

47) Item Type: Fill-in-the-Blank   Objective: 19-2.3
     Level: I   Tag: None

Solar cells convert sunlight into _____ .

electricity

48) Item Type: Fill-in-the-Blank   Objective: 19-2.3
    Level: I   Tag: None

Energy drawn from heated water within Earth's crust is called _____ .

| geothermal energy |

49) Item Type: Fill-in-the-Blank   Objective: 19-2.3
    Level: I   Tag: None

The energy from chain reactions involving nuclear fission is called _____ .

| nuclear energy |

50) Item Type: True-False   Objective: 19-2.4
    Level: I   Tag: None

Usable energy is lost each time energy is converted to another form of energy.

| T |

51) Item Type: Fill-in-the-Blank   Objective: 19-2.1
    Level: I   Tag: None

Cellular respiration produces water, energy, and _____ .

| carbon dioxide |

52) Item Type: Fill-in-the-Blank   Objective: 19-3.1
    Level: I   Tag: None

The contamination of the air, water, or soil is called _____ .

| pollution |

53) Item Type: True-False   Objective: 19-3.1
    Level: I   Tag: None

Pollution can be caused by natural processes.

| T |

54) Item Type: True-False   Objective: 19-3.2
    Level: I   Tag: None

Carbon monoxide is a poisonous gas.

| T |

55) Item Type: Fill-in-the-Blank   Objective: 19-3.2
    Level: I   Tag: None

Pollutants such as smoke, dust, and acid droplets are called _____ .

| particulate matter |

56) Item Type: Fill-in-the-Blank   Objective: 19-3.2
    Level: I   Tag: None

Gasoline, paint thinner, and lighter fluid release _____ into the atmosphere.

| volatile organic compounds |

57) Item Type: Fill-in-the-Blank   Objective: 19-3.2
    Level: I   Tag: None

_____ is the pollutant caused by the incomplete combustion of fossil fuels.

| Carbon monoxide |

58) Item Type: Fill-in-the-Blank   Objective: 19-3.2
    Level: I   Tag: None

_____ comes from petroleum refineries, smelters, paper mills, and coal-burning power plants.

| Sulfur dioxide |

59) Item Type: Fill-in-the-Blank   Objective: 19-3.3
    Level: I   Tag: None

An increase in Earth's temperature due to an increase in greenhouse gases is called _____.

| global warming |

60) Item Type: Fill-in-the-Blank   Objective: 19-3.3
    Level: I   Tag: None

_____ results from the release of oxides of sulfur and nitrogen into the air.

| Acid rain |

61) Item Type: Fill-in-the-Blank   Objective: 19-3.3
    Level: I   Tag: None

_____ is the increase in the amount of nutrients, such as nitrates, in an environment.

| Eutrophication |

62) Item Type: Fill-in-the-Blank   Objective: 19-3.3
    Level: I   Tag: None

_____ is a chemical, used in the paper-making process, that has been linked to an increased risk of cancer.

| Dioxin |

63) Item Type: Fill-in-the-Blank   Objective: 19-3.4
    Level: I   Tag: None

Trash and garbage can be disposed of legally by taking it to a _____ .

landfill

64) Item Type: Fill-in-the-Blank   Objective: 19-3.4
    Level: I   Tag: None

Breaking down discarded material for reuse in other products is called _____ .

recycling

65) Item Type: Essay   Objective: 19-1.1
    Level: II   Tag: None

Explain the difference between a community and a population.

A community is all the plants and animals living in one area within an ecosystem. A population is the group of identical organisms living in a community.

66) Item Type: Essay   Objective: 19-1.2
    Level: II   Tag: None

Explain the difference between a short-term and long-term change in the ecosystem.

Short-term changes are usually easily reversed. Examples are the migration of birds and hibernation of animals during winter. Volcanic eruptions and forest fires produce long-term changes.

67) Item Type: Essay   Objective: 19-1.3
    Level: II   Tag: None

Why is climate an important factor in an ecosystem?

Climate includes temperature, the amount of moisture in the air, and rainfall. These factors determine which plants and animals can survive in the ecosystem.

68) Item Type: Essay   Objective: 19-1.2
    Level: II   Tag: None

Why is interrelatedness a key to understanding ecosystems?

The elements that make up an ecosystem function together. If one factor changes, this will cause another factor in the ecosystem to change.

Chapter 19

69) Item Type: Essay   Objective: 19-2.1
    Level: II   Tag: None

Why is the sun a contributing factor in the production of wind energy?

Wind energy comes from the sun, because different places on Earth receive different amounts of sunlight. This causes variations in temperature, which causes the movement of air known as wind.

70) Item Type: Essay   Objective: 19-2.1
    Level: II   Tag: None

How does sunlight cause water to flow in rivers?

Sunlight heats water in the oceans causing water to evaporate. This water rises into the atmosphere and falls back to Earth as rain and snow. It flows downhill through creeks and rivers back into the oceans.

71) Item Type: Essay   Objective: 19-2.3
    Level: II   Tag: None

What is the difference between the way a fossil fuel power plant generates electricity and the way a nuclear power plant generates electricity?

In both types of power plants, steam is used to cause turbines connected to an electrical generator to rotate. The difference is that the heat is produced by nuclear reactions in the case of nuclear power, rather than by burning coal or oil.

72) Item Type: Essay   Objective: 19-2.4
    Level: II   Tag: None

Explain why energy is wasted in a coal-fired power plant.

Chemical energy is released when the coal burns with oxygen in the air. This energy is used to heat water, which is converted into steam. Not all of the energy is used to heat the water. Some of it is wasted by being transferred as heat to the surroundings. The energy of the steam is used to turn the turbines, but some of the steam energy is wasted.

73) Item Type: Essay   Objective: 19-3.1
    Level: II   Tag: None

What is global warming and why is it a serious problem?

Global warming refers to the gradual increase in the average temperature of Earth. Small changes in this temperature can cause large changes in weather patterns, which in turn may cause drought in some areas, flooding elsewhere, and other environmental disruptions.

74) Item Type: Essay   Objective: 19-3.2
    Level: II   Tag: None

What are some of the dangers to health caused by air pollution?

> Air pollution can make the body vulnerable to respiratory ailments, cause cancer, and hamper the growth and development of fetuses.

75) Item Type: Essay   Objective: 19-3.4
    Level: II   Tag: None

Why is recycling a way of reducing pollution?

> A large cause of pollution is the manufacture of products from raw materials, which means that raw materials must be mined from the ground, grown, or otherwise obtained. Recycling reduces the need to process and transport raw materials.

1)   Tag Name: Figure 19-23

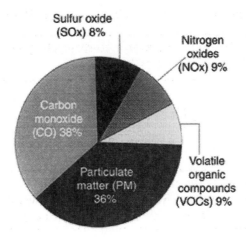

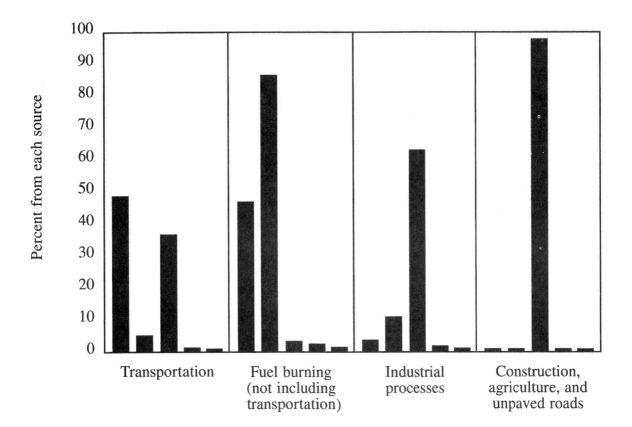

Carbon monoxide, produced mainly from the burning of fossil fuels,
is the top air pollutant in the United States.

327